THE THOUGHT BROKER

The THOUGHT BROKER

BY

SAMUEL McCHORD CROTHERS

BOSTON AND NEW YORK
HOUGHTON MIFFLIN COMPANY
The Riverside Press Cambridge
1928

The Riverside Press
CAMBRIDGE · MASSACHUSETTS
PRINTED IN THE U.S.A.

CONTENTS

The
THOUGHT BROKER

AUGUSTUS BAGSTER, THOUGHT BROKER

In my mail I found a circular marked 'Important,' which seemed to indicate that it wasn't. I was about to consign it to the wastebasket when I saw that it was from an old and valued friend whom I had not met for several years. It was written in that lucidly dictatorial style affected by modern advertisers.

AUGUSTUS BAGSTER

Thought Investment Broker and Banker

Safety and Satisfaction. Why not?

Watch your Intellect grow.

A thought saved is a thought earned.

When you invest in stocks and bonds, you choose your banker carefully. What about your thoughts? Does anybody look after them? Do you know how to select sound and seasoned ideas? Do you know how to invest your accumulated experiences so as to get returns from them? How much wildcat stock have you just now in

your mental safe-deposit? Do you *know* that you
are intellectually solvent, or do you only hope so?
Did you ever have a skilled accountant go over
your intellectual securities and estimate their
present market-value? How much do you mark
off for depreciation every year? Have you any
facilities for coöperative thinking, or do you
hoard your thoughts? What about that big
thought that came to you last summer? Is it
now a part of your working capital, or is it lying
idle? Whatever your goal is, gain it through investments in high-grade thoughts. Let us help
you. Bring your investment troubles to us.
Send for our booklet. Do it now.

After reading the circular, I lost no time
in going down to the financial district to call
on Bagster. I found him on the fourteenth
floor of a big office-building. He greeted me
with his accustomed cordiality, and bade me
disregard the notice on his desk that this
was his busy day.

'What are you up to now?' I asked.
'Something new?'

'Not at all,' said Bagster. 'Same old job
ministering to the unfelt wants of people
who know that there's something the matter
with their minds and want some one to tell
them what it is. It's a common predicament
in this all-too-complicated world.'

'From the sign on your door I gathered that you had taken up with some kind of New Thought.'

'Bless you, no. I haven't a thought that is less than two thousand years old. I never had any originality. I've a good deal of native applicability. I like to apply old thoughts to changing conditions — it freshens them up. When I find people who are muddled I like to help them if I can. That's all.

'The people I am interested in are intelligent persons who have come to the "years that bring the philosophic mind." That is about twenty years after the date set in our educational system for the study of philosophy.

'Touchstone asked Corin, "Hast any philosophy in thee, shepherd?" By that he meant to inquire whether Corin was interested merely in some particular sheep, or whether he liked to talk about the shepherd's life in general.

'We curiously enough set apart for the study of philosophy the period in life when the mind has the fewest facilities for profitable philosophizing. We say to the husky youth, "Go to, now! Stock up with enough general ideas to last your lifetime. Meditate fruitfully on the One and the Many. See things steadily and see them whole. In the 'sessions of sweet silent thought' get acquainted with the Cosmos. Having absorbed large ideas and learned to see things in their true relation, then you may take a few years in the professional school to fit you for your specific job. Just now you must finish up with the fundamentals."

'But the youthful Gallio cares for none of these things. He is not interested in the Cosmos. He is interested in himself. He does not care to sit on the banks of the River of Time contemplating its mighty current. He wants to go in swimming.

'But the chances are that if all goes well with him, and he succeeds in his own business, he will in about fifteen or twenty years awake some fine morning and ask what it is all about. He will be in a mood for philosophizing. John Stuart Mill, speaking of his own education, says, "Anything that could be found out by thinking I was never told until I had exhausted every effort to find it out myself. My father always gave his explanations not before but after I had felt the full force of the difficulties." After about

ten or fifteen years of independent struggle
with circumstances, enough difficulties are
encountered to make the explanations interesting. If even in a small way one has overcome a real difficulty, he is anxious to give
others the benefit of his experience. He
thinks that it forms the basis of profitable
generalization.

'The people I have in mind have accumulated a certain amount of experience. They
have learned to do what they set out to do,
but they have a surplus of unexpended curiosity and energy. Having tended to their
own business, they are ready for larger oper-
ations. They have come, after considerable
effort, upon some thoughts that seem to have
a wide application. They are sure these
thoughts have intrinsic value, but they do
not know what their exchangeable value may
be.

'They are in the same state intellectually
that they would be financially if there were
no banks or exchanges by which the individual's savings could be combined with
others and put to work profitably in large
undertakings. They are even worse off, for
they do not know of any circulating medium
and carry on their intellectual trade by

primitive barter — a mere swapping of ideas. Owing to the lack of coördination, there is a great deal of waste. Many mental factories are running full time, but at a loss. Their facilities for production are greater than their facilities for distribution.

'That being the case, it seemed to me that there was room for the despised middleman. These people need professional assistance. I am not a thinker. I am a thought investment banker and broker. I execute orders and give advice when it is asked for. In my advisory capacity I encourage intellectual thrift. I advise my clients that if their savings are wisely invested, and the accruing interest promptly reinvested, they can be assured of an intellectual competence. But they must beware of bucket shops.

'When a man in the course of his own business comes upon an idea which he is sure has wide applications, he doesn't want to hoard it. He wants to get it into general circulation. He knows it has intrinsic value, but he doesn't know what its exchangeable value may be. "He that is first in his own cause seemeth just; but his neighbor cometh and searcheth him."

'Here, for example, is a man who has made

his fortune in boots and shoes. He knows that business from A to Z. But one day he comes upon an idea that applies first of all to boots and shoes, and then to everything else. He feels like Jack when he began to climb his beanstalk. There seems to be no end to it. It's a principle, and he wants to apply it in a large way. He applies it to Church and State, the public schools and the board of aldermen. The thought expands and almost explodes. He wonders why the preachers and teachers and politicians haven't got on to it. It would revolutionize their methods. In fact, it would revolutionize society.

'Now, if in the first flush of his enthusiasm he were to present his ideas to his business associates, they would think he was a Bolshevik. But if he is so fortunate as to see my advertisement he will come to me and make a few inquiries. What is the present state of the thought market? Is it able without disturbance to absorb so large an offering? I suggest to him that he might be in a better technical position if part of his intellectual capital were in a more liquid form. In a revaluation of his holdings he must be prepared for some paper losses. There is likely to be a difference between the book value of

his stock and the market value. In the case
of unlisted securities there is often a considerable margin between the bidding and the
asking price. All this seems reasonable to
him and we sit down and do a little figuring.

'In estimating the exchangeable value of
an idea, a great many considerations must
be taken into account. The market price of
a thought depends a good deal on who thinks
it. An idea is like a check — its value is
greatly enhanced by the name of its endorser.
Here on the front page of the daily newspaper is an idea endorsed by Mr. J. P. Morgan. Large headlines proclaim its value.
"Never do anything which you do not approve of in order to accomplish something
you do approve of." That is a perfectly
sound proposition. But if the minister of the
Methodist Church in Sauk Centre, Minne-
sota, had said that, as he probably has many
times, it would not have been telegraphed
over the country. When Mr. Morgan says
it, it is news.

'There are useful persons who are not
original thinkers but who are indispensable
in the commerce of ideas. They take
thoughts from one province where they are
cheap and transport them to another where

they are rare. I think that these common carriers should receive some profit over and above the bare transportation charges. A part of the service I render is in facilitating these exchanges, and in analyzing the cost involved in transportation.

'Yesterday a prosperous merchant came to me and, taking a newspaper clipping from his vest pocket, read excitedly: "The 'Manchester Guardian,' commenting on the shipment of cotton goods to Central America, expresses the opinion that the larger purchases of coffee in Germany in recent months contributed to increase the sales of Lancashire products to Central America and Brazil."

'"Here," he said, "is a commonplace in the business world. I wish you'd tell me how to get it over into the minds of the clergymen. It has great spiritual value and it would revolutionize their preaching if they could only be made to see it. My minister has been running a course of sermons on Religion and Modern Civilization. He treats them as if they were trade rivals and the only way were cutthroat competition. Now we business men have got away beyond that. He thinks if he can run down Modern Civilization he can get its custom into the church. He began with a sermon on the Bankruptcy of Science, then he has gone on enumerating one thing after another that has failed — Greek Philosophy, Ethics, and all the rest. When he's got all the competitors out of the way, he's going to wind up with a sermon on Religion, the only hope of a ruined world. I'm afraid that he will get us so in the habit of looking for failures that we shall be discouraged about religion, when we come to it.

"'Now I should like to spring that item from the 'Manchester Guardian' on him, and see how he takes it. When we let up a little on the Germans, they buy more coffee, which allows the people of Brazil to buy more cotton goods from the Lancashire mills, and so it goes. Now doesn't spiritual prosperity follow the same laws? If I had a chance to preach, I wouldn't run down Modern Civilization. I'd boost it. I'd show that Science and Art and Morality and Economics are departments of one Big Business. They help each other when they grow healthfully. I'd make a chart and make every one in the congregation see the point. It doesn't matter where the wave of prosperity starts. It spreads."

'"Why don't you do it?" I said. "You have Laymen's Sunday in your church. Just the chance for you to preach. I can tell you of some mighty good texts."

'I am continually warning people against reckless speculation. I tell them not to believe everything they see in a prospectus. Go slow on any proposition that promises abnormal returns for a small investment. Don't let any one sell you the blue sky. Here is a letter from a man who says he is one of Abraham Lincoln's plain people:

'"I'm a native American and don't care who knows it. Since the war I have accumulated an amount of patriotism that I don't know what to do with. How shall I invest my surplus? What do you think of Hundred-Per-Cent Americanism? Is that too high a per cent for a plain citizen who isn't running for office? Or should I be content with a more moderate return? What about investing a portion of my patriotic enthusiasms in K.K.K., Inc.? I enclose a circular which I have just received. It looks good to me. I don't see where I could get a hundred per cent so easily. I notice that in order to get in on the ground floor I have to be a Nordic. Could you tell me how I can

qualify? All I know about them is that the
Nordics were Protestants from away back
before the Christian era. But were they any
particular denomination of Protestants? Or
does every stockholder get a certificate of
Nordicity when he pays his ten dollars?"

'I answered in a conservative way:

'The securities you mention are highly
speculative. You should look into the history of these offerings and avoid irrespon-
sible dealers. The market for racial and
religious antipathies is very fluctuating. At
one moment it rises to enormous pro-
portions, and then it goes flat. Avoid com-
panies that exploit two kinds of antipathies
at the same time. One is enough. This is
a big country, and you can't corner the
hate market. If you must invest, choose
your antipathy cautiously, then put it away
in a safe place and think no more about it.
Do not expect a ready market for it. Most
persons have antipathies of their own and
don't care to have others dumped upon
them."

'Here is a letter from an excellent and
public-spirited citizen which shows the kind
of questions that come to me. While they
require only a moderate amount of business

sagacity, yet they are not without their difficulties. One correspondent writes:

'"My chief interest has been in enterprises dealing with the peace of the world. Complications in world politics have made it necessary to scrutinize my investments. I ask suggestions from your office. Almost any plan for keeping the peace looked good to me, and in the course of the last twenty years I have invested in pretty nearly everything that was offered. I have taken stock in Hague Tribunal, Benevolent Neutrality, Pan-Americanism, League of Nations (with or without reservations), Outlawry of War, Washington Conference, World Court, Youth Movement, Limitation of Armament, Society of Friends, Universal Religion (when, as, and if issued). I invested in the first issue of War to End War. These were short-time bonds to mature in 1919. When the date of maturity arrived, it was found that no provision was made for meeting these obligations, and an extension of time was asked.

'"As I am loaded up with these securities, which I took in good faith, I am looking for relief. Might not a committee be formed to protect the interest of the investors? I think we ought to consolidate our holdings. Perhaps some of the older pacifist issues might be retired and new issues be presented that would reach a wider investing public. Competitive peace-planning seems as wasteful as competitive armament.

'"Here is an editorial in a paper devoted to the cause of international peace. It bitterly attacks the League of Nations for not interfering in the recent crisis in Egypt, though it declares that if it had done so that would have been the end of the League. 'In our judgment it would have been better for the League to have smashed itself up in a vain attempt to settle the Egyptian question than to continue to exist amid wars and rumors of wars.' What do you think of this as a business proposition? Should the League smash itself up trying to do something that it knows it can't do now, or should it try to keep on as a going concern even though it can't pay dividends for several years? What would you advise me to do with my various holdings?"

'I wrote my client in regard to the advantage of diversified investment. "I would suggest that this is not a time for panic. Do not dump any large block of peace securities on

the market so as to depress it. The fact that
a man like yourself can sympathize with so
many ways of keeping the peace has a steady-
ing effect. It is well to have even the weaker
securities in strong hands. If the whole list
can be kept active, it ensures a continuous
market. You know Sir Philip Sidney used to
advise his friends, 'When you hear of a good
war, go to it.' That was a great encouragement to the sixteenth-century militarists.
Why shouldn't you say, 'When you hear of
a good peace, go to it.'

'"I agree that cutthroat competition between peace plans is uneconomic. We
should remember that the best plan is not
that which looks best on paper. It is the
plan that can be put through. When at last
it is put through it may turn out to be a
combination of various plans, or it may be
an old discarded plan with something added
to make it work. Or perhaps what is needed
is *somebody* who has force enough to work it."

'I suggested also that arrangements might
be made for bringing Peace issues within the
reach of the ordinary man. World peace
seems rather a big proposition for a person
of moderate means. He doesn't know how to
swing anything so big. Now, if peace prin-

ciples in smaller denomination were offered
him, he might feel like investing his little all.
A peace plan covering his own ward might
seem attractive. If he found that he could
carry on a neighborhood church or a town
meeting peaceably, he might be induced to
take stock in more ambitious enterprises.
More attention should be given to the small
investors.

'Perhaps there are no subjects in regard
to which I have had more inquiries from
well-meaning people whose minds are in a
tangle than in regard to the various Temperance issues. They have so overlapped
that it is hard for the ordinary person to find
his way about. There was a time when Temperance was a comparatively simple proposition. Most people would agree in regard to
Ten Nights in a Barroom. The first night
was really enough to convince any one that
a barroom was a good place to keep away
from. But as the Temperance movement has
gone on, it has become involved in many
complexities. Temperance people differ
among themselves, and are not always able
to discuss their differences temperately.
There is often occasion for Father Taylor's
ejaculatory prayer, "Lord, save us from

bigotry and bad rum — Thou knowest which is worse.''

'Here is a letter from an earnest Temperance advocate who feels the need of expert advice. She writes as follows:

'''About 1867 my mother invested in Victory Bonds of Ohio Crusaders. These bonds were to mature in 1880. Before the date of maturity mother was induced to exchange them for W.C.T.U. preferred. I inherited these securities, together with a block of Moral Suasions from my grandmother's estate. They were, I was informed, no longer active on the exchange, but might have some value in the future. From time to time I have taken up the new issues of W.C.T.U. as they came out, particularly the Educationals. I invested in Coffee House, Local Option, Scientific Investigation, Three Square Meals a Day, Better Housing Conditions, Votes for Women, and State-wide Prohibition. I added to my holdings Y.M.C.A., Y.W.C.A., and Social Settlement. I looked upon this as a reasonably diversified investment. The bull movement in National Prohibition took me by surprise, but I promptly invested all my spare funds in Eighteenth Amendment and Volstead

Act. I do not regret this, but I confess that
I have been a little bewildered by later
developments. I don't know just where I
stand, for I am also a D.A.R. and have inherited, from my revolutionary sires, a large
interest in Personal Liberties. Must any of
these valued securities be sacrificed? I have
been advised to sell my old securities for
what they will fetch in the open market and
invest everything in Law Enforcement.
What do you think about it?"

'I wrote to her strongly advising her not
to sacrifice anything. "Law Enforcement is
all right, but it is what we call a business
man's investment. It has to be watched
carefully all the time. It is a strenuous job
to look after it. There are lots of laws on the
statute books, and the law enforcer mustn't
play favorites. I don't think you can afford
to throw away that old-fashioned Moral
Suasion your grandmother believed in. A
little more of it would come in handy just
now. After you have persuaded people to
pass a law you have to keep on persuading
them to obey it. That's the hardest part of
the job in this country. Do you remember
the text, 'What the law could not do . . .'?
There are some things the law can do, but

there are a good many more things that the
law cannot do. They have to be done in a
different way. Don't get in wrong on that
Personal Liberty issue. But insist that Personal Liberty has as its only security Personal Responsibility."

'Speaking of the various temperance reforms reminds me of the reformers of all
kinds who come to my office, and with whom
I have established a brisk business. It is
what might be called a seasonal trade. In his
busy season the reformer has no time to consider the relation of his cause to society as a
whole. He is not a general practitioner like
Hamlet, Prince of Denmark, who could
boast that the world was out of joint and he
was born to set it right. He is a specialist
and confines himself to a particular joint.
He holds on to that with grim tenacity, till
it is set.

'But when his particular reform has been
accomplished the reformer is likely to have
a gone feeling. The cause for which he
labored has triumphed, but it is not *his*
triumph. Its opponents have forgotten that
they ever opposed it. It is no longer a
great moral issue; it has become an accomplished fact, and all the people who stand

for accomplished facts accept it — and then go on as if nothing had happened.

'If the reformer is a sensitive and self-centred person, this is gall and wormwood to him. He is like the workmen in the parable who had borne the heat and burden of the day, and begrudged the eleventh-hour man his penny.

'But if the reformer is a sensible person he comes to my office to talk over the matter just as any successful business man might talk with his banker about changing his investments. He has had a quick turnover. He has cleared a quite tidy sum in his last venture. He has an unexpended balance of pugnacity, and is in a rather speculative frame of mind. He would like to take a flyer in some new cause that conservative people are afraid of. What is there that's most unpopular just now? After talking with me he doesn't lose much time in making the change. One can always find wrongs to be righted if he knows where to look for them. I keep a list in my office of reforms that are overdue. There are some choice bargains yet to be picked up.

'A good many clergymen drop in from time to time seeking advice. They know that they are spiritually solvent, but they are not sure that they are intellectually so. One gentleman complained that he had some seasoned doctrinal bonds for which he had received no return in interest for a number of years. I looked up the securities and explained to him that these bonds had been called some time ago. The capital was safe, but the interest had stopped. The best thing for him to do would be to invest his spiritual capital in some securities that were not callable.

'A zealous minister came with his troubles. He had become, he said, socially minded, but he found it difficult to get his congregation to keep up with him. He had added one social activity after another in his church till the people complained that the addition of another good cause would be more than they could stand. What could he do about it? How could he keep his church up to the mark in social activities, without having it die on his hands?

'I took out a little pamphlet which I had received with the compliments of the United States Steel Corporation. It contained remarks by Judge Gary on the subject of Pittsburgh Plus. "Let's get at the principle. You see, when the steel industry in this country

was in its infancy, the cradle was in Pittsburgh. That's where the steel was actually
produced. It was natural that the price in
other parts of the country should be that established at Pittsburgh, plus the cost of transportation from that point. By and by steel
began to be produced in Alabama and on the
Great Lakes in large quantities. Why should
transportation from Pittsburgh be included
in the price of steel that had never come from
Pittsburgh? Judge Gary explains how at last
the United States Steel Corporation had to
yield to the demand for a new standard for
price-making. The price of steel is no longer
determined by its distance from Pittsburgh,
but there is a recognition of the point where
it is actually produced.

'"Now you are dealing with the same kind
of question. The time was when all social-
welfare activities were centred in the church.
It was the Pittsburgh for altruism. But one
society after another has been organized to
meet special needs. These nonecclesiastical
agencies have proved very effective. You are
going on the principle of the church — your
church — plus. If a person wishes to engage
in work for the community, you expect him
to join your church and then go to work. But

what if he takes a short cut and goes to work
without joining your church? When the
individuals of your congregation join with
their neighbors in good works, you want
them to do all these things over again so as to
make a good showing in your denominational
yearbook. You miss the point of the parable
of the Good Samaritan. He wasn't a good
Jew or a good Christian — he was only a
good Samaritan.

'"Why don't you cut out church plus?
It will save a lot of bother. Your people then
can do their good works in the ways most
natural and efficient without spending too
much time in figuring out who will get the
credit. It will save duplication. It will be
better for the church in the long run. People can have leisure to be spiritually minded
and socially minded at the same time."

'It is not the church people only who are
troubled by the needless duplication of
effort. A well-known philanthropist came
to me for help. He said he had for some time
been converted to the modern view of social
responsibility. He did not consider himself
as a benefactor when he contributed to various organizations for social welfare. It was a
voluntary form of taxation.

'What he objects to is that, now that his principles are known, his assessment has been raised and he is the victim of triple and even quadruple taxation. He asked, "Does the fact that I have given as much as I can afford to one good cause carry with it the obligation to contribute as much to every other good cause? Would there not be a more general participation in altruistic enterprises if the principle of limited liability were recognized?'

'Not only were the demands for money increasing beyond his ability to pay, but also the demands for all sorts of social and semisocial services. During the war he had conducted a number of successful drives. Teams were organized to go through each neighborhood. Two gentlemen appearing where only one had been expected had an intimidating effect on the nongiver. It was an effective method. But of late the number of drives for divers good causes had so increased that the drivers were in danger of collision. "On my last drive," he said, "I carefully chose names of friends with whose generosity and affability I was familiar. When I called at their houses they were out. On my return to my home I found their cards, each friend stating that he would call again to interest me in a philanthropic object to which he knew I would gladly contribute." My client suggested that if well-known philanthropists would subscribe to a gentlemen's agreement not to solicit from one another they might get more from the general public.

'I am organizing a department of domestic relations so that young people and their parents can exchange ideas as to what constitutes propriety. At present the transactions are conducted with the bickering that belongs to private bargaining. Paternalism and maternalism, however necessary in the family, are subject to the law of diminishing returns. Now if the time comes when this is manifest the parents and children could bring their ideas into the open market, and much misunderstanding could be done away.

'There is a great confusion in regard to values. Matters of taste or of fashion are given an inflated moral value. A policy of drastic deflation is indicated for such cases.

'Here is a letter from a young girl. "Dear Sir: I learn that you are dealing in moral exchanges. I wish you would straighten out mother's ideas for me. She is much upset over bobbed hair. Can you tell me how to adjust the matter with her so as to make everything pleasant? She is so solemn about it. Is bobbed hair morally wrong, or is it only unscriptural? If it is unscriptural, where can I find a commentary that explains it the other way? I love mother dearly, but she doesn't understand me. I just have to do something that she doesn't approve of. Perhaps if I knew what she used to do when she was my age, and she wanted to show that she wasn't tied to grandmother's apron string, I might do that. What I want is the equivalent."

'By a curious coincidence I received a letter from her mother, dealing with the same subject. She said that there is a reckless rebelliousness on the part of the rising generation that bodes no good for the Republic. Young people are taking things into their own hands. They won't take advice unless you give them the reason for it, and that isn't always convenient. What is going to become of Civilization?

'I answered in a way to allay her fears about civilization and then to focus her attention upon the immediate problem. In regard to things in general, I recommended some statistical study. A table of statistics is a great stabilizer of the emotions. There is a strong family resemblance among averages. I enclosed a chart prepared by a well-known banking house showing by means of graphic curves the fluctuations of business for the last fifty years. Most people when they hear of good times and bad times have an exaggerated idea of the difference between them. But this chart shows that business sticks pretty close to the normal. What is lost in one way is made up in another. The lowest depression in the worst financial year did not fall fifteen per cent below normal, and in the years of greatest prosperity the rise was not more than that above it.

'I promised to send her a similar chart showing the fluctuation in the manners of the young during a similar period. Our chart had not been completed, but our statistician thinks it probable that the difference between high and low will not amount to more than ten points. There is a complication that has to be taken into account in calculating these averages. Owing to the increased time required for education, the period which is designated as youth has been greatly prolonged. The ladies who took themselves so seriously in the old-fashioned novels were about fifteen years of age. By the time they were eighteen or nineteen they were matrons too much absorbed in bringing up their own children to criticize their parents.

'"Your daughter is evidently irritated because you treat her as if she were younger than she feels, and she retaliates by treating you as if you were older than you are. The years make a barrier between you, and your minds, as the lawyers say, do not meet. She vaguely feels that the time has come when you should meet her more upon a level, and have a decent respect for her opinion. Perhaps she is right. If I were you I would look into the matter.

'"If you wish to establish permanently profitable relations with your daughter, I would advise you to take her into full intellectual partnership, giving her an equal share in all the risks and the profits of your joint undertakings. This sense of responsibility will be good for her. Nor will the difference in value of the contributions you make to the common fund be so great as you may imagine. The book value of your accumulated opinions may be greater, but hers may have the greater marketability. A good deal of your capital is tied up. You have a good many fixed ideas that have value only for their associations. When you clean up all your mortgages you may find that your equity is not large. If you are to develop any new and profitable intellectual business it will be very advantageous to draw on the quick capital which your daughter can furnish.

'"The difference in age need not trouble you. You are aware that in these days less importance is put on the dates in the family Bible. Estimates are now made on the basis of what is called mental age. Call at our office and let our experts determine your mental age. Perhaps when you ascertain it you may look upon your daughter as a contemporary."

'While mothers are likely to be concerned about any deviation from the manners of their girlhood, most of the inquiries from the fathers indicate that they are desirous that their sons should have advantages greater than those which they have enjoyed. Especially is this the case with those who have made their own way in the world. But when it comes to considering what these advantages are there is a great deal of vagueness. Only yesterday a prominent business-man came to ask my advice as to the best college for his son. Knowing that I dealt in intellectual exchanges, he thought I might furnish him with the ratings of various institutions. He brought with him a number of catalogues and I found that he was very much impressed by the colleges that offered the most courses and had the longest list of noted professors.

'"I am looking," he said, "for the college which offers the greatest advantages." "For whom?" I asked. "For my boy, of course."

'"Oh, that simplifies it," I said. "A good many of these advantages in the catalogue are not for him." Then I took up the financial column of the morning newspaper and read: "The capital structure of a company means little to most investors, and yet it is most important. There is a vast difference in investment merit between the common stock of a company that has no bonds or preferred stock ahead of it and the common stock of a concern that has so many other security issues in front of it that it represents nothing more than an attenuated equity.

'"You can figure out how much value to

your boy will be the courses he will never take and the noted professors he will never meet. Perhaps a smaller college in which he could have a larger part might be better for him. In the big college he might have only an attenuated equity."

'I am thinking,' said Bagster, 'of establishing a branch office in Washington. There seems to be a demand for it from conscientious, hard-working members of Congress. Here is a letter which shows a distressing condition.

'"Dear Sir: Seeing your advertisement, it occurred to me that you might be able to do something for a deserving and much misunderstood class of American citizens. They are curiously called Representatives. When I was elected to Congress from the ninth district of my state, I labored under an altogether erroneous notion of what constitutes representative government. I supposed that the people of my district, not having the time or the special knowledge to deal directly with the specific questions that might arise during the session of the national legislature, had asked me to do some political thinking for them. Having the opportunity of listening to the debates and consulting with my colleagues, I could make decisions in regard to matters of which my constituents were ignorant. I now see that this was a great mistake. The alarming increase of literacy, cheap postage, and the radio have undermined the old foundations of representative government. My constituents know more about what is going on in Washington than I do, and they lose no time in telling me so. While I am acting as chore boy, they are making up my mind for me. They tell me how to vote on a bill which I have not had time to consider. I have no longer leisure to read my letters. I weigh them. You would not believe how many pounds of peremptory advice I receive every day. As for telegrams, they are as the sands of the seashore, and they have a curious way of confirming one another. Hundreds of my constituents will rush simultaneously to the offices of the Western Union Telegraph Company and express themselves vehemently in exactly the same language. They do not argue — they decide. The only liberty I have is the liberty of anticipating what they are going to tell me to think. If this keeps on, the government at Washington will be a government by Telepathy.

'"I am not complaining. It is a glorious thought that public opinion can express itself spontaneously on every new question with such terseness and timeliness. But is it public opinion? Who are the promoters who are putting it on the market? There must still be a good many people who have not acquired the habit of telegraphing to their Congressmen. Perhaps some of them rather admire a Congressman who has opinions of his own. Perhaps they would prefer to have him now and then make a mistake of his own rather than make all of theirs.

'"Couldn't you help us out? I wish I could drop into your office and get the current quotations about public opinion, so that I needn't be dependent on the opinions that are wished on me by zealous promoters. If your office were on Pennsylvania Avenue, it would be a great convenience in case an emergency should arise in which I had to make up my mind in advance of telegraphic instructions."'

At this point I interrupted.

'I hope, Bagster, you didn't encourage that Congressman too much. He thinks his constituents have an undue influence over him, and that he could legislate better if they

would let him alone. Perhaps he could.
But this government is not arranged for the
convenience of Congressmen. This is a government not only of the people but *by* the
people.

'By the way, there's a bill coming up for
the benefit of the whole people. We must
get busy and work up public sentiment. It's
your business, Bagster, as well as mine, to
get that bill through at once. I'd tell you
about it if you had leisure, but as you haven't
you must take my word for it. That's the
way I did when it was brought to my attention by persons I have confidence in. We
are at the parting of the ways. Send a night
letter to your Congressman telling him how
much the people around here are wrought
up about it. I advise you to do it now.'

'Oh,' said Bagster, 'I'm here to give advice, not to take it.'

KEEPING UP WITH THE SMART SET IN LITERATURE

BEFORE Tomlinson joined our Literary Society, it was a very quiet affair. We were only a company of friends who met together and read aloud from the literature of the day. We didn't interpret 'the day' too literally; indeed we were inclined to the Biblical idea that one day might be as a thousand years, and a thousand years as one day. If any member came across a good thing, he brought it along and shared the pleasure with us. A trifle like a thousand years since the decease of an author didn't trouble us. We gradually drifted into the habit of reading poetry not because we thought it intrinsically better than prose, but because it was more condensed. Moreover it was particularly adapted for reading aloud. We got more pleasure through the ear than through the eye. We found we could enjoy many of our contemporary poets better that way. We found that their poems sounded better than they looked. In this way we were not confined to the old favorites, but were gradually becoming accustomed to new voices.

That was before Tomlinson joined the society. He came in with a bang. There was an urgency about him which was a little disconcerting to the older members, but we realized that we needed new blood. He gave us his views at the second meeting that he attended. We should look upon ourselves not as a society of antiquarians, but as a poetical current-events club. We should be on a sharp lookout for new genius, and we should aim to be ninety per cent efficient. We should let no gifted man escape. Poetic genius is like a fire: we never know where or when it's going to break out. We must rush to it at the first alarm, and not wait for the heavy critics who are never on the spot till the fire's out. He had noticed, he said, that some of the members had brought in old stuff, some of it published as much as a dozen years ago. We must cut that out. If we were to keep up with the march of literature, we must think no longer in centuries or decades, we must be up to the minute.

He warned us that we must beware of the obvious. Anything that is obviously agreeable is likely to be reactionary. Keats, who in some respects was in advance of his age, confessed as much. He said:

'A thing of beauty is a joy forever;
   Its loveliness increases . . .'

That's why our most up-to-date critics are suspicious of a thing of beauty. People stop to contemplate it and watch its beauty increase, and by so doing they obstruct the intellectual sidewalk. The progressive artist who wants to keep the crowd moving must make it painful for any to loiter too long before his work.

The purpose of poetry, according to Tomlinson, is to serve as an intelligence test. It would never do to have the same test repeated. You could never get at the intelligence quotient that way. If you find you can understand a bit of poetry, then you must try something harder. If we eliminate the easy pieces, he said, we will soon get rid of the dead wood. Those who can't stand the pace will drop out.

Tomlinson spoke in an easy, confident way. He had been taking a correspondence course in salesmanship that guaranteed that he could impose his ideas on others by sheer force of acquired personality. The rest of us hadn't taken the course, so we yielded.

From that day our literary society changed its character. Those who proved unadapt-

able dropped out. Whenever we saw an old
head we hit it. Whenever we heard of a new
verse form, or an example of formlessness, we
studied it. We had no tolerance for the
things of yester-week. We had no longer any
literary background and were glad of it. We
had emerged from the shadow of great names
and were in the open. Tomlinson began to
talk of the New Humanism and assured us
we were 'It.'

Those were great days for the club, when
we could watch a succession of books of
poetry emerge from the Unknown, like
Pharaoh's fat and well favored kine presag-
ing years of plenty. But Tomlinson was
just as well pleased when they were followed
by lean volumes whose meagerness grew on
acquaintance.

'People used to *write* poetry,' he would
say. 'Some do now; but some of the smartest
poets just throw a line or two upon the page,
and let us do the rest. It saves their time
and cultivates our imagination. Here's a
specimen page of a book of poems. It's not
much to look at, mostly margin. You have
to read between the lines, and all around.
The poet is a master of the hiatus. All his
hiatuses are rich and revealing. You will

notice that he begins as if he were going to say something, and then he doesn't. That makes it exciting. It's like watching a man on skis at a winter tournament. He comes like a streak down the icy slide to the jumping-off place, and then shoots through the air for a hundred feet or so. The thrill comes when you see him going off through space, and you don't know whether he will land on his head or on his feet. We must get rid of the old pedestrian traditions and enter into the spirit of the poet Ezra Pound tells about.

'My muse is eager to instruct me in a new gamut or gambetto.
Up, up, my soul, from your lowly cantillations, put on a timely vigor.'

'What is a gambetto?' asked a timid new member.

'It's something the old poets didn't have,' said Tomlinson. 'The thing which this society needs to take to heart is that if we are to keep up with the march of mind, we must put a timely vigor on.

'According to the Freudians a person is either an introvert, or an extrovert. An introvert is always turning his mind in on itself to see what it looks like. An extrovert sits up and takes notice of what is going on outside. Now that explains the different kinds of poetry. An extrovert will look out of doors and describe a rain storm, the drops of water falling on the umbrella, and that sort of thing. An introvert is not interested in a rain storm, but he can make poetry out of his own brain storms. He gives you an instantaneous view of his mind when it is struck by an emotional blizzard.

'We want to study both kinds, just as they come along. Now here is a poem by an extrovert. It's thoroughly objective. The poet doesn't waste any emotion, he just gives a snapshot of what goes on.

> 'I grasped the greasy subway strap,
> And I read the lurid advertisements,
> I chewed my gum voraciously.

'That isn't a very pretty scene, but you are made to see it. It bears the stamp of truth. Now if the poet were an introvert he wouldn't say anything about these details. He would give you an impressionistic view of what was going on in the gum-chewer's mind as he was hanging on for dear life to the strap. It wouldn't be much, but you would get a general impression of mental vacuity. There are flutterings of inchoate sensations. There is a suggestion of intelligence somewhere, like a faint perfume. You can't be sure of it. Perhaps it isn't a thought, but maybe it is. What it is that the gum-chewer has in mind the poet doesn't tell directly. Such brutal frankness would destroy the whole effect. He gives you the impression of what something in the gum-chewer's mind, makes on his mind. Then he leaves you with the impression that it doesn't matter much anyway. It's all very stimulating. If we can only keep our minds limbered up so that we can catch each poem as it comes we'll be all right.

'Let me read what a competent critic says about an admirable new poet: "He has pregnant fragile untouched emotions. His verse has the appearance of perverse abandon, of dizzy falling. There is always the appeal to the motor and visceral sensations, change of position, alarming passive motion — as in an elevator."

'That sounds like something new. The poem makes you have that gone feeling which you have when an elevator drops from under you. The old poets couldn't produce such effects; they didn't have elevators in those days.'

'Do you really like all that, Tomlinson?'
I asked.

'It isn't a question of liking,' he said. 'It's
a question of learning to like what's being
produced. If we are going to encourage the
producers, the consumers must do their part.
If the people in Fresno are to produce more
raisins, the people in Boston are told to eat
more raisins, and they do it. If we are to
keep the wheat farms in North Dakota at
the peak of production, we must eat more
bread. And so if we are to have an American
school of poetry, we must read more poetry,
and read it quick.'

This view of the subject gave me a new
respect for Tomlinson, as I saw that he had a
sense of social responsibility. But it put a
new strain on our critical powers. We felt
that procrastination might be fatal. As Tomlinson said, 'We must appreciate while the
appreciation is good.'

As we were whirled through contemporary
verse I had glimpses of beautiful things over
which I wished to linger. There were ways
of pleasantness and paths of peace. But to
ask Tomlinson to slow down that we might
enjoy them was like asking a motorist to
leave the state highways in order to loiter

along a shady wood road. So we yielded to his will and began to adopt his language of hasty admiration for all that was unfamiliar.

Sometimes I expostulated mildly. 'Don't you think it would rest the club if we stopped to get a bit of perspective?'

'We don't want perspective. What we are after is originality.'

'But what is originality?' I asked.

'It is being different from the way they used to be.'

'But how can we know that we are different unless we know how they used to be? The other day I took up Dr. Johnson's introduction to Cowley and it struck me that the fashionable poets of the seventeenth century might not have been so different from their successors as we imagine. Dr. Johnson says, "They were wholly employed on something unexpected and surprising. . . . Their wish was only to say what they hoped had never been said before. . . . Authors of this race were more desirous of being admired than understood."

'In their headlong search for originality these seventeenth-century poets produced "a combination of dissimilar images, or discovery of occult resemblances in things apparently unlike, and they conceived that to be the highest kind of writing in verse which is chiefly to be preferred for its near affinity to prose. . . . This lax and lawless versification so much concealed the deficiencies of the barren and flattered the laziness of the idle that it immediately overspread our books of poetry, and all the boys and girls caught the pleasing fashion."'

'Dr. Johnson was an incorrigible old Tory,' said Tomlinson.

'Perhaps so,' I answered, 'but in this instance he was talking not about a new fashion, but about one that had for the time gone out. He says, "The fashionable style remained chiefly with Cowley; Suckling could not reach it and Milton disdained it."

'Don't you think we could have a better sense of values in contemporary literature if we had something to measure them by? When an inventor has a happy thought about a mouse trap he employs some one to go to the Patent Office to find out whether there is anything like it there.

'He inquires as to "the state of the art." Of course if we were contented to enjoy a thing of beauty just because it is beautiful we wouldn't mind how old it was. But if it's

this season's novelties we are after, we ought
to make sure they are novelties.'

Tomlinson looked at me with commiseration. 'I see that you are feeling the strain.
All of us do at times. But you mustn't look
back. Remember Lot's wife. Remember
what Washington — or was it Jefferson —
said about entangling alliances. Don't get
entangled with former generations. They had
another set of primary interests — in poetry
as in every thing else.'

'But what if it should turn out that the
primary human interests are the same in all
generations, and it's only the secondary
interests that are different? Let me read
you a bit of Euphues' "Anatomy of Wit,"
which was very fashionable reading in the
sixteenth century. He watches the swift
procession of the books of the day with
eagerness to keep up with them. "We con-
stantly see the booke that at Christmas
lieth bound on the stacioner's stall, at Easter
be broken in the haberdasher's shop. It is
not strange when the greatest wonder lasteth
but nine days, that a new booke should not
endure but three months. But a fashion is
but a day's wearing and a booke but an
hour's reading."

'Euphues expounds the changing taste of the day to his elderly interlocutor and we are told that "Euphues having ended his talk, departed leaving the old gentleman in a quandary." That was just the effect he meant to produce.

'There were some books written in that breathless age that were destined to last more than three months. But I doubt if the author of Euphues knew which they were.'

It was useless to contend against Tomlinson, and our search for literary novelties went on. But after a while the club began to feel the retarding force of the law of diminishing returns. There came a faint suspicion that poets who took pains not to imitate their predecessors might yet imitate one another. People who are living in the same generation, and writing for the same public, cannot escape a certain taint of sameness.

When my turn came to present a new candidate for the Hall of Fame I racked my brain in vain to find some one sufficiently different to satisfy the exigent taste of our little society.

As a refuge from my anxieties I took up a well-preserved copy of Sir Philip Sidney's

'Countess of Pembroke's Arcadia.' I had ventured a number of times into the Arcadia, but had always lost my way in the labyrinth. But this time I skipped the prose and picked out Sir Philip's curious experiments in verse.

With wits sharpened by the tuition of Tomlinson, I realized that here was something that would delight our club by its daring modernity. The chances were that they would never look into the 'Countess of Pembroke's Arcadia.' It would be against their principles.

So I made a few extracts from the less regular poems of Sir Philip Sidney and presented them to the club for consideration.

'You know Sidney Philip, of course?'

Some of the members looked eagerly anxious, as much as to say that they knew him quite well but had forgotten his name. Tomlinson was inclined to be scornful. 'Phillips?' he said. 'He's of the past generation. He edited the "Poetry Review" away back in 1910. He was writing at the beginning of the century. His work is old stuff.'

'Nonsense,' I said. 'I'm not talking about Stephen Phillips, or Wendell Phillips, or Philip of Macedon. If you want something up-to-date, and that tests your intelligence,

you must take up the last thing of Sidney
Philip. It isn't written for the kindergarten
class. Sidney Philip doesn't waste words.
His style has no adipose deposit or con-
nective tissue. He's an artist in words and
doesn't waste his material. He's a post-
futurist as much as any thing. He flings his
nouns and verbs at you, and then it's "Catch
as catch can." The words mean something
to Sidney Philip. If they don't mean anything to you he doesn't care. He's not writing for Main Street. He can take the dictionary just as it stands, and make poetry
out of it. It's great stuff for those who can
appreciate it. Yet I suppose there are not a
dozen persons in this part of the country who
know who Sidney Philip is. That's what
comes of living in a country given over to
common schools, and the Volstead Act. It
isn't conducive to art. Let me read you a
bit from Sidney Philip's last volume, and see
what you can make of it.

'Virtue, beauty and speech did strike, wound, charm
My heart, eyes, ears, with wonder, love, delight
First, second, last did bind, enforce, and arm
His works, shows, suits, with wit, grace and vows.
       Might,
Thus honor, liking, trust, much far and deep,
Held pierced possessed my judgment, sense and will,

Till wrong, contempt, deceit did grow, steal, creep
Bands, favor faith, to break, defile and kill,
Then grief, unkindness, proof, took, kindled, taught,
Well grounded, noble, due, spite, rage, disdain,
But Ah; alas; (in vain) my mind, sight, thought
Doth him, his face, his words, leave, shun, refrain
For no thing, time, place can lose, quench, ease,
Mine own, embraced, sought, knot, fire, disease.

'Now poetry like that is not milk for babes.
It is strong meat for strong men. You must
masticate it. Take the words, one by one,
and let each make its individual impression
on your sensitized imagination. Then turn
your mind into a motion-picture machine,
and run the film through rapidly. Then see
what you've got. When you do it several
times, you'll begin to appreciate Sidney
Philip. He tells us how that poem of his
came to be written in this elusive style. It is
supposed to be written and sung by a young
lady who was very temperamental. "The
verses," says Sidney Philip in his quaint way,
"were with some art curiously written to
enwrap her secret and resolute woes." By
confining herself to a list of disconnected
nouns she was able to sing her secret and
keep it too. The general public could not
guess what it was all about, but to her lover
the detached substantives were exquisitely

meaningful. "The quintessence of each word distilled down into his inmost soul."'

'That's a good suggestion for study,' said Tomlinson. 'Let's take the words as they come and do some distilling. It's time for us to get results.'

'But don't think,' I said, 'that all his work is like that. He's as much at home in prose as in poetry. But when he does write poetry, he is careful not to say anything in an obvious manner. He wants to keep you guessing. He keeps you on the jump. Thus apropos of nothing in particular he says:

'Ah; that I do not conceive, to the Heaven where a mouse climbs.
Then may I hope to achieve grace of a Heavenly Tiger.

'The more you repeat those lines, the more of a mystery they become. Then follows swiftly:

'O sweet, on a wretch wilt thou be revenged,
Shall such high planets tend to the loss of a worm?

'These sudden contrasts between the high and the low are characteristic of Sidney Philip. He doesn't care a rap for the commonplace middle classes. For him it's either the high planets or the worm, the climbing mouse, or the Heavenly Tiger. He doesn't care which it is, so that it's the real thing.

This is an age of extremes, and Sidney Philip is its prophet. It is the age of the soaring airman or the crushed strap-hanger in the subway car.

'Sometimes Sidney Philip uses the familiar forms of versification just to show his mastery of the medium, but even then he manifests the post-war mood of rebellion against things as they are, and even against things as they ought to be. He has all the charming perversity of untrammeled genius. Nothing that he can think of satisfies him. He insists on being consciously pathological.

> 'Like those sick folks, in whom strange humors run,
> Can taste no sweets, the sour only please,
> So to my mind while passions daily grow,
> Joys strangers seem, I cannot bide their show,
> Nor brook all else but well acquainted woe.
> Bitter griefs taste best, pain is my ease,
> Sick to the death, still loving my disease.

'Could anything express more penetratingly the mood of our present-day writers?

'But when Sidney Philip writes as an imagist, he never allows his emotion to intrude. Each image is clear cut and unrelated. There are no entangling alliances with moral ideas. It's pure art. Take this.

> 'O sweet woods the delight of solitariness;
> O how well do I like your solitariness;

Yet dear soil, if a soul closed in a mansion
As sweet as violets, fair as a lily is,
Straight as a cedar, a voice strains the canary birds
Whose shade doth safely hold, danger avoideth her.

'What exquisite **art!** The first two lines strike that note of childish innocence which our best poets use as a foil to their perfect sophistication.

'O sweet woods the delight of solitariness;
O how well do I like your solitariness.

'It's just the kind of poetry a child of eleven would write. It's a class by itself. It puts you in the right frame of mind for what is to follow. Then the images come thick and fast, the dear soil, and the mansion, the violet, and the lily.

'Then comes a line that gives you pause, and tests the quality of your imagination.

'"Straight as a cedar, a voice strains the canary birds."

'"Straight as a cedar" is clear enough. Any one could think of that. But what do you make of "a voice strains the canary birds"? You weren't expecting that? Sidney Philip doesn't explain. There's something exquisitely cryptic in the phrasing. There is a faint suggestion of Chinese influence. I should like to try it on a Mandarin and get his reaction.'

-'It sounds good to me,' said Tomlinson. 'It reminds me of that line of T. S. Eliot, we had such a time over:

'His soul stretched tight across the skies.

'You remember that it took us a whole evening to work that out.'

Finding that Sir Philip Sidney under a slight disguise could satisfy the demands of the club for ultra modernism, I ventured further into the fashionable literature of the Elizabethan and Jacobean periods.

I introduced George Herbert by reading the opening lines of 'Artillerie':

'As I one evening sat before my cell,
 Methought a starre did shoot into my lap,
 I rose and shook my clothes, as knowing well
 That from small fires comes oft no small mishap.'

'That's new to me,' said Tomlinson, 'a star shooting into your lap while you are sitting before your cell, so that you have to get up and shake your clothes. There's something of the Wild West in that young poet. He's the kind that would shoot up the town.'

'Yes,' I said, 'and you'd like his titles. There's nothing commonplace or obvious about them. They don't give you a hint as to what he is writing about. "The Quiddity"; "Superlinary"; "Charms and

Knots." He ties up his words in a knot, and then lets you untie the knot if you can.'

'That's good,' said Tomlinson. 'Let's begin with the "Quiddity," and see what we can make of it.'

'I think we had better leave that for the next time,' I said. 'Quiddities will keep.'

George Herbert's brother, Lord Herbert of Cherbury, gave much pleasure as a daring innovator.

'Here is a little thing of a new man named Cherbury, which I think you will like. It begins:

'Within an open sea of gold,
  A bark of ivory one day I saw
  Which striking with its oars did seem to draw
  Toward a fair coast.'

'That sounds significant,' said Tomlinson.

'Yes; but significant of what?'

'Why it's significant of what it's about. By the way, what's the title of it?'

'The poem is entitled, "A vision of a lady combing her hair."'

'Oh, I get it. The curled sea of gold is her hair; the bark of ivory is her comb, and the oars are the teeth of the comb. That's quite an idea.'

By keeping in the byways of English literature, I think I could have come down to the present day, and provided novelties for the club without awakening suspicion, but after a while Tomlinson became critical. It is just possible that he became a little jealous, and feared that I was setting a pace that he couldn't keep up with.

One day he said, 'Your selection of new authors of the imagist and symbolist school is very stimulating, but I'm afraid the club is getting a little soft. We haven't had enough rough stuff lately. There must be some new writers in Oklahoma that you missed. We'd like something large and virile, and under-worldly, something with the lid off.'

Instigated by his earnestness, I thought I would make a sudden jump into Tennyson, and see what happened. Every one in the club despised Tennyson, who was a synonym for sweetness and all the other childish things we had put away. I should not have ventured on 'May Day,' or 'Locksley Hall.' 'Come into the Garden, Maud' would have been the signal for a riot.

But there was a Darkest Tennyson which might be unknown to Tomlinson. So I said, 'Have you ever come across "The Northern

Cobbler," by Alf Tenterton? If you are looking for some one who is realistic Alf's the boy. He's a man's man. He gives you poetry with a kick. He doesn't care a rap for politeness or prettiness. He doesn't aim to please. He aims to shock, and he hits the bull's eye every time.

'How Tennyson would gasp if he could see how the new generation faces life. You might say it outfaces life.

'The hero of the poem is a regular old soak. He gets drunk every night, and kicks his wife and breaks the furniture, and all that sort of thing. But Tenterton doesn't lay it up against him. He makes you see all the while that the cobbler isn't a bad fellow at heart. It's just his way of working off his inferiority complexes. It's a heap better than having a lot of Puritanical suppressions and taboos. Tenterton is up on psychology, and then he looks at things with the detached eye of an artist. He doesn't mind when the cobbler breaks up the furniture — it isn't Alf's furniture. It's hard on Sally, but then she doesn't come into the picture except incidentally.

'Just see how naturally the cobbler expresses himself. "I coom like a bull loose at

a fair," he says. He just lets himself go.
He's a genuine caveman.

'Once of a frosty night I slither'd an' hurted my huck,
An' I coom'd neck-an'-crop soomtimes slaäpe down i'
    the squad an' the muck:
An' once I fowt wi' the taäilor.

'Now a conventional poet with a standard-
ized mind would have described the battle
as a fist fight; something rather fine and
Dempsey-like. But Tenterton is a realist
and he knew that the tailor wouldn't fight
according to the rules of the ring.

'He scrawmed an' scratted my faäce like a cat, and it
    maäde 'er sa mad
That Sally she turn'd a tongue-banger, and raäted ma,
    "Sottin' thy braäins
Guzzlin' an' soakin' an' smoäkin' an' hawmin' about i'
    the laänes,
Soä sow-droonk that tha doesn not touch thy 'at to the
    Squire;"

'Then follows a strong line:

'An' I looök'd cock-eyed at my noäse an' I seeäd 'im
    a-gittin' o' fire.

'You see there the conscience of the literary craftsman. There's no squeamishness.
If there was anything to smash the cobbler
smashed it. If there was anything to kick
he kicked it. Tenterton's business was to

set it all down just as it occurred. The poem is authentic.

'As for Sally, we see her just as she was, sloppy in her draggle-tailed gown.

'An' the babby's faäce wurn't wesh'd an' the 'ole 'ouse
    hupside down.

'Of course the cobbler felt bad after his spree:

'Like a graät num-cumpus I blubbered awaäy o' the bed,
"Weänt niver do it naw moor;" and Sally looökt up an'
    she said,
". . . thou 'rt like the rest o' the men,
Thou'll goä sniffin' about the tap till tha does it ageän.
Theer's thy hennemy, man, an' I knaws, as knaws tha
    sa well,
That, if tha seeäs 'im an' smells 'im tha'll foller 'im slick
    into hell."'

'That's a strong line,' said Tomlinson. '"Slick into hell!" Tenterton is a little too rough for the "Atlantic Monthly" crowd, but he'll be heard from. He strikes out from the shoulder. You can't keep that kind of fellow down.'

Then the talk fell naturally into self-congratulations over our freedom from the old Tennysonian conventions.

I think I should have established my position as a fearless explorer of the wild frontier of modern literature if it had not been for an unlucky association of ideas. While Tennyson was delighting the cultured Victorian public, Martin Farquhar Tupper was enjoying the rewards of the best seller. The members of the club were accustomed to use his name as a term of reproach, but it was not likely that they had looked into the 'Proverbial Philosophy.'

As there was a ruder Tennyson who would delight the admirer of the caveman in literature, why should there not be an esoteric Tupper to reward the lover of the wilfully obscure?

I introduced a new author who should be nameless. 'He is just trying out his instrument, but he shows promise. He is a rebel not only against all literary traditions, but also against all previous and all contemporary rebels. He scorns ordinary verse patterns, yet he uses them as it suits his purpose. He takes over the whole field of knowledge by right of eminent domain. He delights in paradoxes which he clothes in language so demure that the undiscerning public accepts them as truisms. But beneath the demureness there is a sardonic spirit that laughs bitterly and vanishes. There is a subtle irony which masquerades as commonplace.

The humor is so dry, that it seems to belong to the permanently arid belt. Then there are sudden sublimities for those who like such things. It's like being in an aeroplane. One minute you are running along the ground, and then suddenly you are off into the sky.

'Let me read you these lines on seaweed:

'The sea-wort floating on the waves, or rolled up high
      along the shore,
Ye counted useless and vile, heaping on it names of con-
      tempt;
Yet it hath triumphed gloriously, and man has been
      humbled in his ignorance.
For health is in the freshness of its savor, and it cum-
      bereth the beach with its wealth
Comforting the tossings of pain with its violet-tinctured
      essence,
And by its humbler ashes enriching the proud.

'There's what I call an intriguing kind of poetry. Some of it you can understand. You have seen the seaweed heaped up on the beach, and you may have sufficient agricultural knowledge to be aware that its ashes have value as a fertilizer, or as the writer cleverly puts it, alluding to the Cape Cod farmer, "by its humbler ashes enriching the proud." You visualize the humble seaweed, and the proud farmer.

'But what do you make of the previous line?

'Comforting the tossings of pain with its violet-tinctured essence.'

I read the line slowly, watching the reaction of the club members.

'This line,' I said, 'is intriguing. We all recognize its beauty. "Violet-tinctured essence," contrasts poignantly with "the tossings of pain."

'Even if the words mean nothing in particular, they are very precious.

'But what has the "violet-tinctured essence" to do with common seaweed? Perhaps it hasn't anything to do with it, but if we should find out that it has, there would be an added pleasure which comes with intelligence.

'But perhaps we had better go back to the vivid phrase "tossings of pain." Perhaps you have had a touch of erysipelas which has caused the tossing of pain, and perhaps it has been relieved by the application of iodine. You can visualize the bottle. Now all that you need is a very slight knowledge of pharmacy to make the poet's meaning sun-clear. When you learn that one of the chief sources of iodine is common seaweed, you are on a perfect intellectual equality with the poet. The rather sloppy seaweed on the beach is glorified by its relation to the violet-colored essence in the bottle. It is a process which the psychoanalysts call subli-mation.

'You ask, "Why doesn't the poet explain all this?" The answer is, "He does, in a footnote, and that is the reason why I have been able to explain it to you."'

That was an unlucky moment for me. The reference to the footnote was my undoing. I glanced at Tomlinson. There was a strange look on his face. It was not scorn or indig-nation, but a look of outraged innocence. Tomlinson seemed as one who was wounded in the home of his friends.

'Martin Farquhar Tupper!' he exclaimed. '"Proverbial Philosophy," footnote to page 14.' His tone conveyed deep respect for an honored name, and sorrowful surprise at the liberty I had taken with it.

As we walked home, I broke the silence which had become painful. 'Tomlinson,' I said, 'I didn't know that you read Tupper.'

'I don't,' he said, 'in public, but what a man does in private is something between himself and his conscience. One has to keep up with the procession in literature as in everything else; but it's hard on the nerves. The mind is kept on the stretch. It's the price we have to pay for progress. But when I go home from the Literary Society and sit down by the fire to enjoy myself, I always take up the "Proverbial Philosophy." It's a link with a happy past. Makes me feel at home with my own mind. He tells me what I knew beforehand, and it's very comforting to be told it in such a serious way. It makes me feel safe and sane. In these last few years when I've felt that it was my duty to keep up with the literary advance movement, I've craved something I can understand without too much effort. Now I can usually understand what Tupper is driving at. And when he makes an allusion that is a little difficult all one has to do is to look at the bottom of the page.

'For instance take the poem on memory, which begins:

'Where art thou, storehouse of the mind, garner of facts
    and fancies,
In what strange firmament are laid the beams of thine
    airy chambers?
Or art thou that small cavern, the centre of the rolling
    brain
Where still one sandy morsel testifieth man's original.

'I shouldn't have guessed what that small cavern was, or what was the sandy morsel in the rolling brain, if it hadn't been for the footnote, which explained that "the small cavern is the pineal gland, a small oval about the size of a pea, in the centre of the brain, and generally found to contain, even in children, some particles of gravel. Galen and afterwards Descartes imagined it to be the seat of the soul."

'That shows what Tupper had in mind. After that, it's all clear sailing, though I don't know what the new physiologists would say about that piece of gravel in the centre of the brain. Galen, I suppose, is looked upon as a back number in medicine.

'When I'm reading the text of Tupper, I don't tax my memory with the words. It's the general impression that everything is all right that I retain. But when it comes to a footnote I take notice. I'm sure to get some useful information. That's where you slipped up. If you had just recited the poetry, you might have got away with it; but when you quoted the footnote I spotted you. I can repeat every footnote in the "Proverbial Philosophy."'

'I'm sorry, Tomlinson, that I made such a bad break.'

'I'm sorry too,' he replied. 'I'm afraid it will break up the club.'

ANGLING IN THE POOL OF OBLIVION

OF all forms of sport, angling is the most esoteric. Well does Walton call it the contemplative man's recreation. The angler is not only contemplative himself, but he is the cause of contemplation in other men. To a super-contemplator, sitting on a breezy hilltop, he is the subject of curious speculation. There he is in a superlatively damp place, surrounded by pestering mosquitoes, waiting for an accident that may not happen. Nothing that he can do seems to accelerate the crisis. No tempting variety of bait can ensure success against the procrastination of the slow, unwilling trout. Nor does he know that the trout is there. This may be his day out.

Wherein is the joy of this long trial of predatory patience? Why should a man spend the best part of a spring day dangling an unavailing hook over an unresponsive pool? Where is the sport?

To such a question the cheerful angler, returning with an empty basket, deigns no reply. He has the inner satisfaction that comes from an eventless day well spent. He believes in the values of what the sagacious Bismarck called 'the imponderables.' There are no scales in the fish market that could weigh the trout he was angling for. He does not believe that the pool was untenanted. He has been trying his wits against the Fabian tactics of a shrewd old antagonist. Tomorrow he will try again. Hope deferred does not make the heart sick. It affords a healthy satisfaction.

This is the kind of pleasure some of us get in angling in that dark pool of oblivion that is called the Past. Our ordinary experience is with our contemporaries, but sometimes we like to wander off and try our luck in antiquity.

We pore over an ancient book, and for a long time nothing happens. The words arrange themselves according to the pattern of our own day. We discover facts, but they are dead facts. And then something happens. There is a sudden pull as of a living thing struggling in its own element. It is alive and fighting. There is a thrill that rewards us for our hours of watchful waiting. There is a swift motion beneath the surface, which is communicated to us and becomes a

part of our present experience. Something
that happened long ago is happening again
in our consciousness.

There is a sense of immediateness, as if
the barriers of time were suddenly removed.
We are not looking back at the Past — we
are looking around at what is passing. It is
all present to us. It is a momentary glimpse
of a living reality; we must be quick about it
or it is gone. The word 'moment' means
movement. The present is that instant of
time when everything is presented to us as
moving rapidly before us. The procession is
passing our house, and the band begins to
play.

This experience is something different from
the knowledge of what is called 'History.'
It is not so much historic as subhistoric. The
contemplative man uses history as an angler
would use a motor car to take him swiftly
over the state road to a point in the woods
where he leaves the highway to plunge joy-
fully into the wilderness, where he can loiter
and enjoy himself in his own way. He is not
interested just now in the course of events
or the sweep of great causes; he is not curious
of the grandiose things which are matters of
careful record, but of the forgotten emotions

of half-forgotten people. Suddenly some one
who had been a mere name becomes a real
person and is caught in the act of doing something interesting.

> Oh! the battle of the Nile —
> I was there all the while.

That is the way we like to feel. We have the
sense of being a part of the performance.

I do not agree with the dictum of Mr.
Henry Ford that 'History is bunk.' But the
historian will be the first to admit that history as set down in a book is not what many
people think it is. It is not a record of all
the important things that happened during
a particular period. It is an arrangement of
selected facts, and the historian is responsible
for the selection.

He may do his best to rid his mind of
prejudice. But he has an ineradicable prejudice in favor of intelligibility. He tries to set
down the facts in such a way that their relations may be readily understood. They are
marshaled in an orderly fashion. Unfortu-
nately that is not the way they happened. So
for the sake of an intelligible narrative he
must eliminate those happenings that were
irrelevant, confusing, and incoherent.

His history must be the history of some-

thing and not of everything. In spite of himself he must select his facts. He is the potter
with power over his clay. Some facts and
persons he chooses for vessels of honor and
some for vessels of dishonor. The clay cannot say to the potter, 'Why hast thou made
me thus?' A history book is a manufactured
article. It is assembled and put together by
competent workmen, like a Ford car. It is
made to go, and if it won't go it is scrapped.

The historian deals with great masses and
long periods of time, and he is apt to ignore
the fortunes of the little people. The individual is but an atom. Still, the atom exists
as well as a planet, and an atom can get
along without a planet easier than a planet
can get along without its atoms. The saucy
little atom, with its galaxy of electrons re-
volving within it, is imperturbable. Its
atomic weight is what it is, and its attrac-
tions and repulsions are all its own. It will
join huge and temporary aggregations of
matter, but always on its own terms, and
with reservations. Secure in its littleness it
says to the big Universe, 'I stand for the
self-determination of atoms. Thus far thou
shalt go and no farther. No more pushing,
no more crowding. I require but little space,

but that space is my own and I propose to fill it.'

The idiosyncrasies of atoms are not to be despised. The historian describes epoch-making events and is apt to take for granted that the people who were participants or eye-witnesses were as much impressed by them as he was. But how could they, poor fellows, be expected to know which events were to have historical importance and which not? There are any number of events which promise to be epoch-making that turn out to be false alarms. Whose fault is it? The event, in bridal array, starts at the church door, waiting to be joined to the new epoch. The fickle epoch delays his coming, and finally weds another event.

'It is one of the bad effects of living in one's own time,' wrote Horace Walpole in 1759, 'that one never knows the truth about it till one is dead.' Future generations, he said, would take it for granted that everybody at that time was absorbed in the fortunes of Frederick the Great and the world-wide war. But they weren't.

'A war that reaches from Muscovy to Alsace and from Madras to California don't produce an article half as long as Mr. John-

son's riding three horses at once. Europe is
a dull, insignificant subject to one who knows
little and cares less about Europe. Even the
King of Prussia, except on post days, doesn't
occupy a quarter of an inch in my memory.
He must kill a hundred thousand men once
a fortnight to put me in mind of him.
Heroes who do so much in a book, and seem
so active to posterity, lie fallow a long time
to their contemporaries. And how it would
humble a great prince who expects to occupy
the whole stage to hear an idle man in his
easy-chair cry, "Well, why don't the King
of Prussia do something?"'

Even amid events of the most tremendous
importance the trivial has a way of taking
the centre of the stage and holding it for its
brief moment.

In the supreme crisis of the World War,
Sir Edward Grey, Mr. Balfour, and Mr.
Lloyd George hurried across the Channel to
consult with the French Government. What
were their thoughts as they returned? One
of them repeats their conversation. Sir Edward Grey: 'I could not help thinking of
mines all the way over.' Mr. Lloyd George
(wearily): 'Oh, I was feeling too bad to
think of mines.' Mr. Balfour (with con-

vincing emphasis): 'I longed for a mine.'
This is not the pattern that the historian
chooses, but it is the stuff that human life is
made of. In the stream of consciousness all
manner of things float by. Most of the little
things are forgotten, but when they are acci-
dentally called to memory they enable us to
produce a scene, and give it reality. They
give just the touch of incoherence that
makes it akin to our daily experience. We
feel that we have an instantaneous view, a
picture that has not been retouched.

The Apostolic times seem far away, and
Saint Paul is an heroic figure moving rapidly
through the ancient Roman Empire. I see
him through the mists of time. But I ask
myself how I should have reacted to his
presence. Were I among those who listened
to him, should I be astonished at his doctrine? Should I reject it or enthusiastically
accept it? What I do not consider is that
my reactions would largely depend upon
circumstances.

I take up the book of the Acts of the
Apostles. 'We sailed away from Philippi . . .
and came unto them to Troas in five days;
where we tarried seven days. And upon the
first day of the week, when we were gathered

together to break bread, Paul discoursed
with them . . . and prolonged his speech
until midnight. And there were many lights
in the upper chamber, where we were gathered together.'

Now I can feel that I am a part of the company. We all came to hear Paul. But the
plain fact is that he has been preaching too
long. It is midnight and the room is crowded.
and there are too many lights.

Then when he goes on, unconscious of the
passage of time, our attention is distracted.
'And there sat in the window a certain young
man named Eutychus, borne down with
deep sleep; and as Paul discoursed yet
longer, being borne down by his sleep he fell
down from the third story.'

We who are there have our minds distracted. When we look up and see the young
man, in his precarious situation, beginning
to nod, our attention turns away from the
Apostle. All our sympathies are with Eutychus. The secondary figure takes the
first place in our consciousness. The chances
are that when afterward our friends begin
to discuss their favorite preachers, and one
says, 'I am of Paul,' and another, 'I am of
Apollos,' we take the part of the brilliant

Greek orator. This is only because we heard
Apollos under more favorable circumstances.

These discrepancies of judgment are the
very essence of contemporaneousness. We
appeal to Posterity to reduce everything to
certainty. But Posterity is somewhat ab-
sent-minded, and is likely to confuse its
own troubles with those of the generation it
is judging. It is enlightening to see things
while they are happening. Always there is a
mixed multitude watching the mixed happenings with mixed emotions or with no emotions at all. There are those who take sides
fiercely and those who take sides mildly and
those who look on with bovine incuriosity.
They are never all excited at the same time
or over the same thing.

In the last great battle of Armageddon
there will doubtless be noncombatants stroll-
ing over the field asking languidly, 'What is
all this about?'

It was so in the first battle of Armageddon, described so vividly by Deborah, the
prophetess: 'The kings came and fought;
then fought the kings of Canaan in Taanach
by the waters of Megiddo.'

There was no lack of martial ardor. 'Zebu-
lun and Naphtali were a people that jeop-

arded their lives into the death in the high
places of the field. ... The stars in their
courses fought against Sisera.' There was
much shouting of the captains, and 'then
were the horsehoofs broken by the means of
the prancings, the prancings of their mighty
ones.'

But the enthusiasm was not universal.
The tribe of Reuben looked on with indiffer-
ence, being chiefly interested in the wool
industry. Reuben, 'why abodest thou among
the sheepfolds, to hear the bleatings of the
flocks?'

Why indeed? I should like to interview
an honest Reubenite, and discover why he
preferred to hear the bleatings of his flocks
rather than the noise of the battle.

'Gilead abode beyond Jordan: and why
did Dan remain in ships? Asher continued
on the sea shore.' And these were the people
of Meroz, who, in spite of the bitterest in-
vectives hurled at them, insisted on pre-
serving a benevolent neutrality.

It would appear that at the battle of
Megiddo, in that far-off time, there were all
sorts of people, and they reacted to the
questions of the hour in all sorts of ways.
There were pacifists, militarists, profiteers,

pro-Canaanites, agriculturists, and imperturbable seafaring folk, while above all was
heard the shrill voice of an emancipated
woman.

'Awake, awake, Deborah: awake, awake.'
She was awake, and she succeeded in awak-
ing some, but not all. There was a great difference of opinion. To some the battle was
the most important in all history; to others
it was a regrettable interruption to trade.

When we are traveling rapidly through a
foreign country we see crowds and classes,
and when by chance we are introduced to
individuals we treat them as types. We
unconsciously multiply them and draw con-
clusions as to the group to which they belong. Only when we have been long enough
in one spot to feel at home do we see particular persons clearly differentiated.

Wordsworth complained that Scott in one
of his novels misquoted his lines on Yarrow.
'He makes me write:

> 'The swans on sweet Saint Mary's Lake
> Float double, swans and shadow.'

Wordsworth had written 'still Saint Mary's
lake' and wished to emphasize its stillness.
'Never could I have written "swans" in the
plural. There was one swan and only one,

and that is the reason I recorded the Swan
and the Shadow. Had there been many
swans I would have said nothing about
them.'

This is something to be remembered by
those who are dealing with the literature of
a former age. When we discover a lifelike
individual it is better to see him as he is
without jumping at the conclusion that
there were vast multitudes just like him.
Perhaps he was an exception. Why not
enjoy him as he is? There are times when
one swan vividly seen makes a deeper impression on the imagination than a dozen
swans accurately counted. And the same
thing may be said of geese.

In Ben Jonson's 'Volpone, or the Fox,'
we come across Lady Would-Be, who with
her husband, Sir Politick Would-Be, is on
her Italian journey. She is a very advanced
lady, with a great contempt for all conventions and taboos. She is anxious that every
one shall know how sophisticated she is.
She has arrived in the advance guard of the
intellectuals.

> I have a little studied physic; but now
> I'm all for music, save in the forenoons
> An hour or two for painting. I would have

A lady, indeed, to have all letters and arts,
Be able to discourse, to write, to paint,
But principal, as Plato holds, your music,
And so does wise Pythagoras, I take it,
Is your true rapture.

As for poetry, she dotes on it. All the poets
are at her tongue's end.

Petrarch or Tasso or Dante?
Guarini? Ariosto? Aretine?
Cieco di Hadria? I have read them all.

But chiefly she admires the poet who
'has so modern and facile a vein, fitting the
time. . . . Dante is hard, and few can understand him. But for a desperate wit there's
Aretine. Only his pictures are a little
obscene.'

Lady Would-Be plunges at once from the
latest poetry into the latest philosophical
speculation, choosing by preference to dwell
on those things which 'overwhelm the judgment, cloud the understanding,' and finally
'assassinate our knowledge.'

Poor old Volpone cries, 'Some power, some
fate, some fortune, rescue me.' Now if
one were writing an historical thesis Lady
Would-Be might be taken as a type of early
seventeenth-century culture. It would be
safer to say she was a character that amused

Ben Jonson. If Ben Jonson were alive to-day he might find the same kind of amusement, if he knew where to look for it.

I take up a history of the Protestant Reformation. I get a general idea of the course of events. I read of the dissolution of the monasteries, the new learning, and all that. But how did people feel when all these changes were going on?

Then I take up Stow's 'Survey of London' in the time of Queen Elizabeth. I am taking a walk with an amiable and intelligent gentleman whose only intent is to show me the interesting sights before it is too late. For London is in a state of transition.

Once London was full of springs and brooks. 'There were wells, sweet and wholesome, frequented by scholars and youths of the city on summer evenings when they walked forth to take the air.' There was Clerkenwell, 'where the parish clerks used to assemble and play some large history out of Holy Scripture.' That has all passed away — more's the pity! The parish clerks no longer assemble to play some large Scriptural drama. The new theater is changing all that.

'Once the wall of the city was all about

furnished with towers and bulwarks in due distance one from the other.' But all this picturesqueness is being rapidly destroyed by the march of improvement.

I begin to feel differently about Elizabethan London. I feel its ruthless modernism and realism in contrast with the picturesque past. That is the way the Elizabethans felt.

Stow begins to talk about education as any gentleman of mature years would speak. In these days there are a great many educational fads, and the schools are being revolutionized, but for all their pretentiousness it is a question whether they make better scholars than they did when he was a boy. As for the disputing of the scholars according to the rules of logic, that has been discontinued. 'I myself in my youth have yearly seen, on the eve of Saint Bartholomew, the scholars of divers grammar schools repair unto the Church in Smithfield, where upon a bank boarded about, under a tree, some one scholar both stepped up and there opposed and answered till he were by some better scholar overcome and put down, and then the newcomer, taking his place, did like as the first, and in the end the best opposers

and answerers had rewards, which I observed
not but that it made good schoolmasters and
good scholars.'

Now I get a glimpse of the way in which
people actually felt when the new learning
was crowding out the mediæval scholasti-
cism. It was not a matter that interested
only the great scholastics we read about. It
was a matter which affected every school and
the proud parents whose sons got prizes in
those exciting contests which were conducted
like our old-fashioned spelling bees. If I had
in my youth stood up under a tree on Saint
Bartholomew's eve and astonished the whole
village by my precocity, and had been the
last on that glorious day to be argued down,
I would not listen to the radicals who were
trying to introduce a newfangled intelligence
test. Wait till these educators produce
scholars of the old type — which they never
did.

We take a walk through a large street
recently replenished with comely buildings
and go out to the Whitechapel region.
Stow calls attention to the fact that Whitechapel is not what it used to be. It is becoming sophisticated. We pass the new
church of Saint Botolph. 'The parishioners

being of late years mightily increased, the
church is pestered to find seats for them.'

To get into the country, let us take Hog
Lane. 'This Hog Lane, within these forty
years, had on both sides fair hedgerows of
elm trees, with bridges and easy stiles to
pass over into pleasant fields very commodi-
ous for citizens to walk in, and shoot, and
refresh their spirits in the sweet and wholesome air, but now is turned into a continual
building of garden houses and small cottages,
bowling alleys, and suchlike, as far as Whitechapel.'

In this region that is now being built up
Stow can remember rural delights that are
no more. 'There was a farm at which I myself in my youth fetched many a halfpenny
worth of milk and never less than three ale
pints for a halfpenny in the summer, nor less
than one ale quart for a halfpenny in winter,
always hot from the kine, as the same was
milked and strained. One Trollop and afterwards Goodman were the farmers there, and
had thirty or forty kine to the pail.'

Now Trollop and Goodman are not historical characters, but they are very real
persons to me, which is more than can be
said of many who had greater names. I can

see their burly figures at milking time. I
sympathize with Stow in thinking that it was
a pity that when the elder Goodman died his
son did not follow in his ways and keep the
thirty cows and sell milk to thirsty pedestri-
ans at three pints for a halfpenny. Instead
of which young Goodman, when he came
into possession, yielded to the prevailing
fever for real-estate speculation. He sub-
divided his farm into city lots and thereafter,
says Stow, instead of being an honest yeo-
man, moved into the city and lived like a
prince.

That sort of thing I see to be happening
all the time. And the worst of it is that nobody knows how to stop it.

When I walk about with Stow and see all
the fine old abbeys dismantled, and think
of the way the fair old elm trees in Whitechapel have been cut down, and think how
much better a man old Goodman was than
his popinjay of a son, I begin to feel reactionary. Three or four hundred years from
now there may be historians who will take it
all coolly, but they won't know what we know.

Stow takes me by the Priory of the Holy
Trinity, which was scrapped. It was Sir
Thomas Audley who did it. He sold the bells

for what they would fetch, which wasn't much. Then he offered the priory church and steeple to whoever would take it down, but no man would take the offer! Stow remembers when this sort of thing was going on all over London. 'At that time any man in the city could have a cartload of hard stone brought to his doors for sixpence or sevenpence with the carriage.'

We come in our walk to the old church of Saint Andrew Undershaft, on Cornhill. Stow explains the name. There was an immense timber shaft or pole which every May Day was set up in front of the church, and when it was thus placed it was higher than the church steeple. Chaucer had written of the great shaft in Cornhill, testifying of the ancient union of mirth and religion. It had not been raised since 1517, but it rested on six hooks till the third year of King Edward VI, 'when Sir Stephen, curate of Saint Katharine's, preaching at Paul's Cross, said this shaft was an idol.' Sir Stephen cried out against the name of the church. That was the kind of man he was. 'He would have fish days any day but Friday, and Lent at any time except between Shrovetide and Easter. . . .

'I have ofttimes seen this man, forsaking
his pulpit in the said church, preach under a
high elm tree in the midst of the churchyard,
and entering the church, forsaking the al-
tar, sing Mass in English on the tomb of the
dead toward the north. I heard his sermon
on Paul's Cross, and I saw the effect that
followed; for in the afternoon of that present
Sunday the neighbors and tenants over
whose doors the said shaft had lain, after
they had dined to make themselves strong,
raising the shaft from the hooks on which it
had rested two and twenty years, they sawed
it in pieces, every man taking his share.
Thus was that idol, as they termed it,
mangled and afterwards burned.'

When I watch the proceedings and remember how Chaucer had chuckled over the
thought that the Maypole was higher than
the church steeple, I have a dislike for
thin-lipped, sour-faced Sir Stephen. Why
couldn't he leave our Maypole alone? Why
wasn't Saint Andrew Undershaft a good
enough name for our church? Our fathers saw
no harm in it. And then to think that those
hypocrites sawed the Maypole up and carried it to their own homes! If they had made
a jolly bonfire in the street and danced around

it we could have forgiven them. But the pious rogues carried their sticks to their own fireplaces, where they could show their hatred of idolatry and save their fuel bills at the same time.

When I read of the religious persecutions of those days I find it hard to realize what they were like to the people who engaged in them. I think of one side as habitual martyrs and the other side as habitual persecutors. I do not take into account the fact that these parts were changed with the utmost alacrity.

But one day I drop in at the trial of Bishop Hugh Latimer in the reign of Queen Mary. It is all so different from what I had expected. It isn't a criminal trial. It is a spiritual tournament, a grammatical exercise, and a revival of religion, all in one.

I see the old Bishop 'holding his hat in his hand, having a kerchief on his head, and upon it a nightcap or two, and a great cap with two broad flaps to button under the chin, wearing an old threadbare Bristol frieze gown, girded to his body with a penny leather girdle, from which hanged by a long string of leather his Testament and his spectacles, which were without a case.'

He has just come from his prison and is
weak physically, but he has the fighting
spirit. He is a knight, lance in hand, ready
for all comers. There is a sharp clash of
texts.

Weston. 'Where do you find that a woman
should receive the sacrament?'

Latimer. 'Will you give me leave to turn
to my book? I find it in the eleventh chapter
to the Corinthians. I trow these be the
words. *Probet autem seipsum homo.* I pray
you, good master, what gender is *homo?*'

Immediately the assembly is in an uproar.
Weston, Cole, Harpsfield, and Feckenham
begin to shout their answers. Latin grammar was a live subject in those days, and
angry passions were aroused. Weston cries,
'Marry, it is common gender.' Feckenham
asserts, 'It is *probet seipsum*, indeed, and
therefore it importeth the masculine gender.'

In the first round Latimer has the best of
it. Weston finds a new passage of Scripture
and begins the battle anew.

'"I will be at host with you anon"! When
Christ was at his supper none were with him
but the Apostles. Ergo — he meant no
woman.'

Latimer. 'In the twelve Apostles was re-

presented the whole Church; in which you
will grant both men and women to be. Well,
remember that you cannot find that a woman
may receive by Scripture.'

I can hear a deep voice crying, 'Master
opponent, fall to it!' In those days pugnacity and piety were not strangers. Latimer is plucky, but he is an old man, and
when he is pushed too far he admits his weakened powers.

Latimer. 'Disputation requireth a good
memory. My memory is clean gone and
marvelously weakened, and none the better,
I wis, for the prison.'

Weston. 'How long have you been in
prison?'

Latimer. 'These three quarters of this
year.'

Weston. 'I was in prison six years.'

Our preconceived ideas of persecutor and
martyr do not cover this situation. Weston
is as proud of his six years in prison for conscience' sake as a soldier would be of the
battles he had fought. These men understood each other. They were of the same
bulldog breed. Our doctrine of toleration
would have seemed to them to be very
flabby.

When he comes again before the commissioners, Latimer asks, 'Will your lordship give me leave to speak a word or two?'

Bishop of Lincoln. 'Yes, Master Latimer, so that you use a modest kind of talk without railing or taunts.'

Latimer expounds his faith and ends with 'Now I trust, my lord, that I do not rail yet.'

Bishop of Lincoln. 'No, Master Latimer, your talk is more like taunts than railing. What was that book you blame so much?'

Latimer. 'It is by one which is Bishop of Gloucester, whom I never knew, neither did I at any time see him, to my knowledge.'

'With that the people laughed, because the Bishop of Gloucester sat there in commission.'

Then the Bishop of Gloucester stood up and said it was his book.

Latimer. 'Was it yours, my lord? Indeed I knew not your lordship, neither did I ever see you before, neither yet see you now through the brightness of the sun shining betwixt you and me.'

'Then they all laughed again.' The Bishop of Lincoln commanded silence.

Then they all laughed again! This was not the Spanish Inquisition. The laughter was

the laughter of sixteenth-century Englishmen who were accustomed to give and receive hard blows. When they had laughed
for a moment they would take up the cud-
gels again. To-morrow would be a time for
grim tragedy; to-day they would fight the
good fight.

In the preceding reign, a Protestant states-
man was asked to fulfill engagements made
by King Henry VIII. He answered bluntly:
'That was made by the King of England who
now dead is to the King of France who now
dead is. Then was then, and now is now.'

That is the practical man's dictum. Then
was then and now is now, 'and never the
twain shall meet.' What happened then is
nothing to us. What happens now will be
nothing to those who come after us. But the
contemplative man is not satisfied with this
bleak view of Time. Now is now; but he is
interested in thinking about how our now
will appear to our successors. What is there
that will be found to have permanent interest? How will our fashions appear when
they have become old-fashioned? Which of
our institutions have survival value? He is
accustomed to project his thoughts into the
future and to think of now as if it were then.

In like manner he takes delight in sudden glimpses into the life of other days. He does not conceive of that life as altogether outside his personal experience. There is for him a dramatic revival of old comedies and tragedies. They have been enacted before, but it is his privilege to see them presented again on the stage of his imagination. Perhaps some of the actors will be more kindly received and more fully appreciated than on their first appearance.

To help us to reset the stage, to recall the actors, to turn on the lights, and to enjoy the play — this is the aim of a liberal education.

But after all, every man must be his own stage manager.

PROPOSALS FOR A SOCIAL SURVEY
OF LITERARY SLUMS

THERE are few fields that social reformers, armed with instruments of precision, have not entered. They have investigated tenements, country houses, stables, cotton mills, slaughter houses, match factories, steel works, churches, and universities. There are better business organizations to raise the standards of business, wholesale and retail. Things sanitary and things industrial and things intimately domestic are looked into by persons trained for the purpose. The individual is not allowed to go his own way. The public is recognized as a party in interest. The world is being made safe for the working man. Sickness is not a private matter. The guardians of the public health are not content to notice the general facts of morbidity and mortality. They seek the causes. Without regard to the prejudices of the householder, they poke into ash cans and dark closets, measure the width of alleys, test the plumbing, call attention to articles left on the fire escape, make notes on wages, compute the number of hours lost by reason

of illness, inquire into the profits of land-
lords, and ascertain the number of arrests
for juvenile delinquency.

But there is one class that has been
strangely overlooked by investigators. It is
the class of literary workers — the makers of
books, magazine articles, poems, plays, and
the like. These articles are manufactured in
great quantities and are looked upon as
necessities by that portion of the community known as the 'literates.' But the hard-
working industrialists who produce these
wares have hitherto been immune from investigation. Literary people have long been
known as 'the irritable race,' and their natural irritability has been increased by every
attempt to impose non-literary tests upon
them. They have insisted on complete inde-
pendence. If a work is good from a purely
literary standpoint, they say that is enough.
Whether it is an offense against good morals
or an outrage against good taste makes no
difference. The clever author claims the
rights of extra-territoriality. Literature sets
up its own courts, and claims to be a law
unto itself.

But literary artists cannot expect to be
let alone any more than the rest of us. When

there is so much salutary curiosity about the number of bacteria in the milk, can the public be expected to be indifferent to the dangers that lurk in the inkstand?

I was therefore not surprised to find that a society has been formed to investigate the conditions under which literary work is performed, to safeguard the health of the workers, to study the occupational diseases to which literary people are subject, and to keep consumers informed of the facts. The society is well organized, with national headquarters and regional superintendents and a large and highly respectable advisory committee.

I have before me a pamphlet published by the society, entitled 'Proposals for a Social Survey of Literary Slums.'

Let me say at once that any one who takes up the circular with the expectation that it will gratify the slumming instinct will be disappointed. Personalities are avoided; there is no directory of objectionable literary characters. The evident aim is scientific, and there is no attempt at the sensational. Indeed a considerable part of the circular is given over to an appeal for funds. This is a necessity in all enterprises of an educational character and tends to stabilize them. One who appeals for funds will never put his proposals in so radical a form as to alarm the large contributor.

Leaving out the financial appeals, I will give some quotations which will show the nature of the new proposals:

While so many social agencies are investigating labor conditions, it is not strange that the public should be unaware of a quiet and painstaking work that is going on in the study of literary slums and their effect on the public health. Indeed, it is the policy of our association to avoid publicity, and only the urgent need of more funds to carry on our investigation has led us to make any publication at this time. Every one is aware of the good work which has been done for a number of years by the Consumers' League. That society works upon the assumption that the consumer has a right to know the conditions under which the goods he buys are manufactured. It makes it its business to supply necessary information and to insist upon proper standards. This is in the interest of both producer and consumer.

But hitherto nothing has been done for

literary workers. We have followed the theories of early nineteenth-century individualism, rather than the philosophy of the twentieth century with its emphasis on social welfare. Very little attention has been paid to the unemployed or unemployable, or to the plight of the casual worker, or to those whose occupation is only seasonal. Such a problem as the juvenile delinquencies of poets has hardly been touched. There is a lack of statistical information on many vital points.

More than a hundred years ago Shelley wrote:

'A poet there was who sat by a ditch,
    And he took an old cracked lute,
And he sang a song that was more of a screech
    'Gainst a woman who was a brute.'

At that time such a case would be looked upon as one for private commiseration, though even then it must have been evident that what the poet needed was not alms but a candid friend. But by the socially minded person of our day, the case cannot be so easily dismissed. And when a score of poets sit by a ditch and give a combined screech, we recognize the fact that we are dealing with a social question. It is necessary to investigate the ditch, and examine the old cracked lutes.

The literary critic of the old school is like the judge at a cattle show who judges according to the points the cattle breeders have agreed upon. But the modern representative of the State comes to the owner of a herd of fancy Jerseys and insists on looking them over. He cares not a fig for the blue ribbons, but insists on applying the tuberculin test.

Literary persons, when there is any talk of outside interference with their calling, raise the cry of Victorianism or Puritanism. This is barking up the wrong tree. The Puritan would object to a book because it was unscriptural. The Victorian would object to it because it shocked the proprieties. The social investigator asks, What is its ascertainable effect on the mind of the reader? This is pure fact-finding, and should be carried on without prejudice. No preconceived theory must be allowed to interfere with the experiments. We must be prepared to accept new evidence when it is presented.

It used to be supposed that clothing worn by yellow fever patients carried the disease. Experiment proved that this was not the case. It used to be supposed that unpleasant looking water was always unwholesome and clear water was safe. Now we send the sparkling water from a suspected spring to be analyzed.

A book does something to us. It may put us to sleep, it may infuriate us, it may inspire us, it may depress us, it may make us feel that life is not worth living and that the bottom has dropped out of the universe. The author may say that this is none of his business. He lives for his art, and what happens to us is no concern of his. We answer, You may be right. It may be none of your business, but it is very much our business. When we put food in our mouths, it is not for the encouragement of a temperamental grocer. It is because we think that it is good for us. The food must agree with us and not merely with him.

It is the same with what we put into our minds.

> 'That book is good
> Which puts me in a working mood.'

That is what I read it for. I do not propose to sacrifice my intellectual health for the sake of another man's art. My mind may not be of the first order, but it is the only one I have, and I can't afford to sacrifice it.

The case of Typhoid Mary is familiar to all social workers. This excellent woman, who was herself immune, went about innocently diffusing typhoid germs. She was a carrier. In a way she was not to blame for her exceptionally strong constitution, but the fact that she herself enjoyed good health made her all the more a menace to the community.

Compare the careful investigation that discovers such a carrier of disease with the way we treat a book that is under suspicion. One person reads a book and declares that it is immoral; then another person reads it to see if it is as bad as it was reported to be; then a large number of persons who have not time to read the book discuss it acrimoniously. Then the emancipated critics say that, if it is suspected of immorality, that is *prima facie* evidence that it is a work of genius. Then the careful parent says that, at any rate, it is not the kind of book to be put into the hands of his daughter. Then his daughter tells him that he needn't worry. She read it last summer, and any one who is still talking about it is 'dated.' Then the discussion begins all over again, with a more recent book as the point of departure.

Such antiquated discussions would not be tolerated in any district conference of the Family Welfare Society. Even the most inactive Board of Health would not approve canned goods suspected of containing ptomaines, because one of the members admired the picture pasted on the cans. They would test the food in a scientific way instead of waiting for the result of a *post mortem* on one of the consumers.

A New Testament writer declares that evil communications corrupt good manners. But only careful experimentation can determine to what extent and under what conditions these communications can be made through literature. Cold print is not a good culture medium for certain sins. Just why this is so we have not ascertained — we only note the facts.

Thus our experts have made a careful study of two thousand detective stories to ascertain their effect upon the conduct of their readers. The readers investigated were judges, magistrates, bankers, bishops, and other clergy who by their own confession were addicted to this kind of literature. Contrary to what might have been expected, there were no reports of crimes against life and property that could be traced to such midnight reading. Our investigations seem to point to the probability that the specific germs of burglary, murder, arson, and piracy are not viable in printed matter. They require personal contacts. At any rate, it is obvious that certain classes of the community have a high degree of immunity.

On the other hand, an investigation of the effect of so-called sex novels reveals a real danger. In dealing with it, however, the public should have more expert advice than that usually at the disposal of legislators. The law can only deal with passages that are 'shocking.' It is much less dangerous for the moral sensibilities to be shocked than for them to be lulled to sleep by an insidious poison.

The real watch and ward must be like that which Edmund Spenser described as kept in the stately House of Temperance:

> 'Within the barbican a porter sate,
>   Day and night dewly keeping watch and ward.
>   Nor wight nor word mote passe out of the gate
>   But in good order and with dew regard;
>   Utterers of secrets he from thence debared,
>   Babblers of folly and blazers of cryme.'

To be safe, each mind must have its own warder, and it will not do to hand over his work to the Chief of Police.

Leaving each individual free in matters of taste, and refusing to interfere with his personal affairs, our commission confines itself to the matters which concern the public. We wish to ascertain the causes of literary diseases, rather than to deal merely with symptoms. The reading class is dependent on the labor of the writing class. It has a right to know how the other half lives. It must be able to discriminate between literature that is produced under wholesome conditions and that which is the product of the slums.

What constitutes a slum? It is not simply a place where poor people live. Poverty can be clean, self-respecting, and healthy. But the poverty of the slums is of a different kind. It is the result of overcrowding. There are too many people herded together, too little light, too little air, too little wholesome food, too little opportunity for recreation. Human beings crowded together are stunted. There is no room for the full development of personality. All sorts of morbidities and abnormalities appear.

Nobody plans a slum, and therefore it is hard to get anybody to feel responsibility for it. It is a condition that comes when there is

no intelligent planning. Hence the need of
socially minded people to point out actual
conditions. It was discovered that some of
the worst slums in London and New York
were owned by excellent people who were
unaware of what was going on. Even
churches have often been guilty of gross
carelessness in this respect.

Many persons would be surprised to know
how many books there are that are produced
under slum conditions. They are the product
of minds that are overcrowded, under-
nourished, and with a shameful lack of ven-
tilation. When a number of slovenly minds
are working in close contiguity, the results
are deplorable. They have no leisure to
grow wise, and quickly lose any desire to be
so. Yet they are very prolific.

The results of overcrowding and under-
nourishment are apparent in the history of
literature. The reader of the 'Dunciad' —
and every one should read the 'Dunciad'
once a year — is familiar with the recrimina-
tions of the literary proletariat of the reign of
Queen Anne. It is evident that literature
was recognized as a sweated industry. There
were too many poets competing with one
another for a precarious living. The notori-

ous slum called Grub Street was literally
swarming with young persons who had come
to London to live by their wits. There were
penny-a-liners waiting for such hack work
as might be offered by the printers; there
were versifiers with a pretty knack of turning
off complimentary odes; there were pam-
phleteers, strong-arm men, literary bravos,
who could be hired by great men to do their
dirty work. Then there were private brawls
carried on with much ink shed.

The impression we receive is of a feverish
struggle for literary existence, a terrible pressure of the poetical population on the means
of subsistence.

Pope writes:

> 'When sick of muse our follies we deplore
> And promise our best friends to write no more,
> We wake next morning in a raging fit,
> And call for pen and ink and show our wit.
> For those who cannot write and those who can
> All rhyme and scrawl and scribble to a man.'

We recall Swift's familiar lines:

> 'Every creature
> Lives in a state of war by nature.
> Each poet of inferior size
> On you shall rail and criticise.
> So naturalists observe a flea
> Hath smaller fleas that on him prey

And these have smaller fleas to bite 'em
And so proceed *ad infinitum*.
Thus every poet in his kind
Is bit by him who comes behind
Who though too little to be seen
Can tease and gall and give the spleen.'

Thus, he says, they 'lay Grub Street at each other's door.'

The Industrial Revolution changed all that. Grub Street has been improved out of existence. Literature, like everything else, has felt the effect of the factory system and the manifold efficiencies of big business. The industrious writer shares in the benefits of quantity production, standardization of products, better marketing methods, and up-to-date advertising. Without waste motion, he can turn out an unlimited number of short stories with interchangeable parts, and of perfect uniformity. Nothing is left to the curiosity of the reader, who knows just what he is buying. All this is in the interest of intellectual economy.

But though the Industrial Revolution has accomplished so much, the evils of overcrowding are still painfully manifest. Wherever too many persons of the same kind crowd together, slum conditions are bound to be created. It doesn't matter what they are trying to do — if there are too many of them they get into each other's way. In the Middle Ages many of the larger monasteries fell into a slummy condition. Too many people were trying to be good without allowing each other sufficient elbow room, and they made a mess of it. Theodore Parker used to say to his brother ministers in Boston, 'Ministers are like cabbages — they don't head well when they grow too close together.' Even college professors feel the need of a sabbatical year when they can get away from their own kind.

Nowhere are the effects of overcrowding more painful than among literary workers. Their mentality suffers from too close proximity. Under such circumstances, their minds do not stand alone. They tend to stock together in a glutinous mass. After a time they come to pride themselves on their intellectual stickiness.

From time to time epidemics sweep through the congested districts of literary centers. They are often mistaken for significant movements, and the more nervous intellectuals are alarmed for the future of civilization. But the illiterates and semi-literates who live in the open country go their way as if nothing had happened. Their immunity is very fortunate for the race.

Just now there is an epidemic almost exclusively literary — which is characterized by excessively low spirits. The talented writers indulge in the most lugubrious prognostications. Their tone is consistently querulous. They feel in duty bound to resist any tendency to joy, freedom, resiliency. Whether in prose or verse, they take dismal views of the present and of the future. The only comfort they allow themselves is in the thought that the past was probably still worse. They cultivate the sardonic, and refuse any little alleviations that may be suggested by the natural man. What strikes one is the singular synchronism in their emotions. They utter their shrill lamentations, as if they were obeying a cheer-leader. A single person who felt that way might be interesting, but there are too many of them. These birds of a feather flock together — all moulting at the same time.

We have watched these cases with considerable solicitude. Our commission is investigating the environmental influences which tend to depress the spirits of the literary worker. Our agents who have been dealing with child labor have made some valuable suggestions. The great objection to child labor is that by subjecting nerves and muscles to a premature strain, the victim is deprived of that elastic strength necessary for the varied activities of manhood.

It is suggested that many writers are stunted because they have been set to tasks too great for their mental age. Their faculties have not been given time to mature, and they have tried to express what they have not yet experienced. There is evidence of malnutrition. There is gristle where there should be bone. There are many symptoms of intellectual rickets. When the author tries to be more clever than he is, the effort is bound to tell upon him. Many a promising novel has been spoiled by premature publication. The author has not allowed sufficient time for the book to catch up with the jacket. He should be reminded of Lord Chesterfield's remark that a wise man is as careful to live within his wit as he is to live within his income. Here is a field in which our society is undertaking welfare work. We have opened up a department of preventive literature.

Charles Lamb wrote a discriminating

essay on the 'Melancholy of Tailors,' but he did not suggest that the melancholy infected the suits they sent out from their shops. But the melancholy of poets gets into their poems, and it is catching. Unlike burglary which, as we have said, does not seem to be spread through literary media, a tired feeling is easily communicated from the writer to the susceptible reader. Hence the need of isolation.

As contributors like to have a little human interest injected into the reports of societies they are prepared to support, we have ventured to insert a letter which we have received from one of our most resourceful case workers. We may remark in passing that she left a position in the English Department of a well-known college for women to enter the employ of our society. We hope that a generous public will make it possible to retain her services. She writes:

'My time has been taken up with a young poet who seems worth saving and who was sent to us by one of our friendly visitors. He was naturally of a buoyant disposition, but when composing poetry he was plunged into abysmal gloom. When the writing mood was upon him, he would fairly revel in the

thought of the futility of effort. His emotions were unstable. At one moment he
would be in a verbal paroxysm of grief over
the thought that things are as they are, and
the next moment he would be in stony despair over the suspicion that they weren't
that way at all. Nothing pleased him. The
shorter the poem, the worse he seemed to
feel. He would start as if he were going to
cheer up and say something. Then he would
stop in the middle of an unpunctuated sen-
tence as if to say, What's the use? Two or
three ejaculations on an otherwise empty
page produced the effect of frustrated genius. It was the effect he intended to produce. And yet, as I said, he was naturally a
cheerful and companionable young man.

'I made a thorough investigation and
found that he had confined his reading to the
verses of other poets who were in the same
condition. It was a case of competitive
world-weariness.

'He was removed from his unfavorable
surroundings to a hill farm in Vermont,
where he could be under observation and
at the same time move about quite freely.
The slender volumes which had infected him
were taken away. The only book allowed to

remain in the house was an old copy of Walt Whitman's "Leaves of Grass." For the first few weeks the poet was irritable, and wandered about trying to think of some disagreeable subject to write about. He exercised his ingenuity by giving a sinister twist to any ordinary theme. This he did by attaching dismal adjectives to normally cheerful nouns. He wrote a poem in free verse, entitled "Coal-black sunshine." I remonstrated with him and told him that sunshine isn't coal black. It made no difference to him. "That's what most people think," he said. "But I'm not writing for the crowd. This is no Pollyanna stuff."

'Then he wrote on — "The jealous earth turns green, or the recurrent tragedy of Spring." "When the tired arbutus trails." "Why the gentian is blind." "When the tainted well went dry." This last theme seemed to have great possibilities. By first lamenting its taintedness and then lamenting its drying up, he got gloomy thoughts coming and going.

'Being in New England, he thought he would write on, "The deserted farmhouse." But all the farmhouses in the vicinity had been transformed into attractive summer

cottages and seemed remarkably cheerful.
But he found melancholy satisfaction in
thinking of the city he had left behind, and
wrote a drab little piece entitled "The deserted flat." He pictured a disillusioned
summer boarder sitting under an apple tree
and thinking in dry-eyed despair of his
deserted flat in the city. He pictured its
loneliness and stuffiness in a sweltering
August day. To be sure, nobody was in it to
suffer, but it was material for melancholy
reflections.

'But in the course of a few weeks, sep-
arated from his companions, a change came
over him. One day he came from the
orchard with the "Leaves of Grass" in his
hands.

'"Do you know, I was looking for a title
for a new book of poems. I thought that
Walt would have something for me. I found
it, or thought I found it. Here are the lines:

'Ah! Poverties, wincings and sulky retreats,
    You degradations, you tussles with passions and
        appetites.'

That sounded good to me. How would this
do for a title? 'Poverties, Wincings and
Sulky Retreats.' Perhaps the publishers
would want a short title. 'Sulky Retreats.'

That's what we sophisticates are in favor of.
Or perhaps just 'Wincings.' That would
look stunning on the title-page.

'"Then I read on and found that Walt
didn't look at these things as our set does.
After giving a list of the degradations, he
seems to think that it's not necessary to
wallow around in them. He thinks we not
only ought to get out of them as quickly as
possible, but that we can. This is what he
says:

'Ah, think not ye finally triumph, my real self has yet
    to come forth.
It shall yet march forth, overmastering till all lies be-
    neath me.
It shall stand up, the soldier of ultimate victory.'

'"Then I read on and found that that was
what he was driving at all the time. 'Out of
the bulk, the morbid, and the shallow,' he
says, there comes something that is 'electric,
antiseptic.' It's that antiseptic element that
our crowd seems to have missed. Listen to
this:

'Over the mountain growths disease and sorrow
    An uncaught bird is ever hovering,
    High in the purer, happier air.
    From imperfection's murkiest cloud
    Darts always forth one ray of perfect light.
    Oh, the blest eyes, the happy hearts,
    That see, that know the guiding thread, so fine
    Along the mighty labyrinth.'

'"The poet, according to Walt, is not the one who is lost in the mighty labyrinth and sits down to bewail his fate. He is the one who has found the thread and is following it. If that is so, it makes quite a difference. I want to take time to think it out. At any rate, I'm going to scrap 'Wincings' and 'Sulky Retreats.' I'm going to call my next volume, 'The Soldier of Ultimate Victory.' Don't you think that's a good title?"

'"Yes," I said, "if you can live up to it." Seeing that he was in a more genial mood, I ventured to say:

'"Now that you've got a new line on Whitman, perhaps you might be more sympathetic with Milton's ideas in regard to the nature of poetry."

'I found I had gone too far.

'"We've cut out that old Puritan stuff long ago."

'"I was only going to recall to your mind Milton's declaration that poetry is 'simple, sensuous, and passionate.'"

'"Did he say that poetry ought to be sensual? I didn't suppose he was as advanced as that."

'"Milton didn't say *sensual*," I replied; "he said *sensuous*. He thought poetry made its appeal through the senses. It's something that you feel and hear and touch and taste and smell. The poet's senses become avenues of joy. He writes about

> 'Such sights as youthful poets dream
> On summer eve by haunted spring.'

The poet has a power of visualization and has the ability to make us see through his eyes. His words are a sort of incantation. Just look at that bend of the Connecticut where Brood Brook comes in through the meadow. I could see it by myself, I suppose, but I get a great deal more pleasure out of it when I murmur Milton's lines:

> 'Meadows trim with daisies pied
> Shallow brooks and rivers wide
> Towers and battlements he sees
> Bosomed high in tufted trees.'

There aren't any towers and battlements here, but look at that farmhouse on the top of the hill on the New Hampshire side — 'bosomed high in tufted trees.' How the youthful poet would have enjoyed seeing that!

'"And the poet enjoys not only familiar sights but familiar sounds. He loves to listen

'While the ploughman near at hand
Whistles o'er the furrowed land
And the milkmaid singeth blithe
And the mower whets his scythe.'

And there are times when the smell of new-mown hay gets into his verse, and it is none the worse for that. Milton, when he was your age, enjoyed these sensations. He treated poetry as if it were a privilege and not an affliction. Don't you think there is something in that?"

'"Perhaps so," said the poet hesitatingly, "but in these days we have to be sincere. The public expects it of us."

'"Quite so," I said, "but suppose you stay up here till you get rid of the jangle in your nerves. Some fine morning you will wake up and be sincerely glad that you are alive. If you succeed in expressing your sincere gladness in language that is not sophisticated or fantastical, but in words that are simple, sensuous, and healthfully passionate, the public will be glad too."

'"But don't you think if I were as simple as that I might lose my standing among the new poets?"

'"Ah!" I said, "people won't ask whether you are new or not. They will just recognize you as a poet."'

Another epidemic which sweeps through congested literary areas is what may be called pseudo-primitivism. It shows marked periodicity and recurs, with variable virulence, at intervals of thirty years. It is in its nature atavistic, being characterized by a relapse into modes of expression once quite natural but long since outgrown by the more civilized part of mankind. There is a literature that is genuinely primitive. It expresses primitive passions in a simple and unself-conscious way. There is also a literature which deals with a society that is more or less sophisticated. Each has its own place. But the writer whose mind has not had time to mature tries to be primitive and sophisticated at the same time. When a number of primitivistic-sophisticates, or sophisticated-primitives, get together and encourage each other in their calculated indiscretions, they become disturbers of the peace.

Here the experience of our social workers in the slums is of great value. Nowhere can the mental processes of sophisticated-primitives be better studied than among the youthful denizens of the slums. Here is a kind of knowingness that is utterly divorced from wisdom. In the crowded streets the play instinct of boys finds its only expression in dodging policemen and risking life in stealing rides on passing vehicles. The victim of such an environment finds an impish pleasure in the forbidden. Humor degenerates into a crooked wit. There is a shallow sophistication of the streets. The qualities which the street boy admires are agility, hardness, toughness, sharpness, and a vivacious insolence. These are the qualities that stand high in the estimation of the gang.

When we see literary reputations made by the exhibition of these qualities, we have reason to believe that we are dealing with the gang spirit. A popular literary gangster can go far. He has a scorn for reticence which endears him to his own kind. He would return to Nature, but never in a teachable spirit. He is one more object that Nature must apologize for.

While coarse natures harden under the pressure of crowds, more sensitive spirits are distracted. This forms a separate problem. This brings us to something that our commission has much at heart — the guarding of our more promising and sensitive literary workers from what Emerson called 'the insanity of towns.' There is a tendency for all industrialists to leave the countryside and flock into the urban centers. This creates social problems. To no class is the lure of the city more perilous than to the man of letters.

Our commission is making a study of the effects of city life with its various stresses and strains on literary workers. We have begun with a survey of New York City and shall continue our researches in other centers so far as our funds will allow.

A study of current literature produced by clever writers who have crowded into Manhattan Island impresses us with the contrast to the spirit of Diedrich Knickerbocker when he set out to write the history of New York. Knickerbocker began with the creation of the world and came gradually down to his own time. His idea was that Manhattan Island was only a part of the Universe and could only be understood in relation to it.

Not so with many of the writers of the present Manhattanese School. To them life in New York seems to be not a normal growth, but a series of premature explosions. The firecrackers have short fuses. There is a sensation of jumpiness. There is rapid motion, but no sense of direction. There are all kinds of noises, all kinds of people, all kinds of events. In order to be up to the minute, one must grab the minute before it becomes antiquated. The person who is content to work while it is called to-day must look out lest what he calls to-day may be what his more agile competitors call day before yesterday. One feels as a piece of innocent white paper might feel while being thumped by the keys of the typewriter. The clicks and thumps follow each other rapidly. They probably mean something, but the typist has no time to explain to the paper what it is all about. Perhaps she doesn't know herself. She is taking dictation that is too rapid for her.

The writers whose work conveys the impression of futile hurry and undue nervous strain are not the interpreters of the great city, but its victims. To see a modern city aright, one must be able to look at it as he looks at a great mountain, or a stormy sea, with a certain detachment. He must not be distracted by its varieties or irritated by its noises or bullied by its threats. His must be the 'harvest of a quiet eye.' If you wish to enjoy the sublimity of Niagara, the best way is to take your stand on the bank. It is a mistake to think that you can get a better impression by going over the falls in a barrel.

At this point the writer of the pamphlet remembered once more his official duty and made an urgent plea for annual membership, with especial emphasis on the virtue of promptitude.

THE WORM TURNS

FOR some time there had appeared in the newspapers vague reference to a mysterious personage known as the Grand Vermicularius. He was the head of a secret society which had sprung up very rapidly and had ramifications throughout the country. Its objects were unknown and its membership carefully concealed. It was supposed to be strong on propaganda and to be boring from within. The new organization held no public meetings, announced no programme, made no threats. But it was hinted that the members of the I.O.T.W. might be found in all churches, parties, labor unions, colleges, public schools, and chambers of commerce. The minister of your church, the senior warden, the editor of your daily newspaper, might be affiliated. Even the wife of your bosom might be enrolled as an auxiliary without your knowing it. For while the initiated had their secret signs and passwords by which they were known to each other, they were pledged to silence as to the order when they were in the presence of outsiders. This secretiveness was terrifying to an open-minded democracy.

Even the Grand Kleagle was alarmed over an empire more invisible than his own. Of late several elections had turned out differently from the way they had been planned by astute party leaders. It was suspected, though not proved, that the Grand Vermicularius had something to do with these political mishaps.

The title of the potentate had led many people to consult the dictionary. 'Vermicular,' as an adjective, was defined as 'like a worm in form or movement, tortuous, sinuous, writhing or wiggling.' This threw little light upon the nature of the society, but conveyed the impression that its chief officer was a dangerous character.

Various patriotic orders became alarmed and began to send warnings through the mails that there was a vast society doubtless financed by foreign gold and aimed at the very heart of the Republic. They did not know just what it was, but that made the peril more imminent.

All this aroused my curiosity and I determined to have an interview with the Grand Vermicularius. How this interview was finally brought about it is needless for me to relate.

I confess that it was with some trepidation that I came into the presence of this formidable personage of whom I had heard so much. I had formed an idea of what he was like. I had pictured him as a dark saturnine man with black hair and bushy eyebrows, and eyes, such as I had often read about, that bore you right through and reveal your innermost secrets, while all the time retaining their own inscrutability. I had rather expected to be seated in such a way that a single ray of light would fall upon my telltale countenance while he sat in semi-darkness.

But when the Grand Vermicularius received me in the sitting room of his modest house on Elm Street all my preconceived notions were shattered. There was an air of imperturbable domesticity in his surroundings. There was not a suggestion of the conspirator or the autocrat. His appearance was that of the ordinary business man of the better type. His manner was frank and friendly, and he entered into conversation like one who has nothing to conceal. 'I suppose,' he said, 'that you want to know about our new order. If you want to find out about our passwords and ritual I have nothing to tell. But if you want to know about our objects and princi-

ples I am glad to give you information. The
I.O.T.W.— which, being interpreted, is the
Independent Order of Turning Worms — is
made up of people who have been ignored
and trampled upon and misrepresented till
we can't stand it any longer. We have become class-conscious. We demand redress of
grievances. We have turned!'

'So I have understood,' I said; 'but what
class do you represent?'

The Grand Vermicularius went to his
bookshelf and, taking down a volume of Milton, read, '"That hapless race of men whose
misfortune it is to have understanding."
That's us!'

'Oh, I see what you are driving at,' I said.
'You represent the militant intelligentsia.
You think the intelligent minority should
assert itself against the stupid majority. It
is too bad that, where there are so few men of
superior ability, they shouldn't be allowed to
rule over the other kind. I suppose you agree
with Mr. Mencken about the unconscionable
number of yokels and morons and nitwits
who can always outvote the men of understanding.'

'You have totally misapprehended my
meaning,' said the Grand Vermicularius with

a touch of asperity in his voice. 'When I identified myself with the men of understanding, you don't think that I set up for a superior person! The class I represent is the majority in this country. We are people of plain understanding. We are neither morons nor yokels; neither are we geniuses, bigots, or fanatics. We are people who mind our own business, accept our responsibilities, and are more or less aware of our limitations. We support the churches and schools, and at the same time try to improve them; we pay our taxes, not without some grumbling; we serve on time-consuming committees, and do all sorts of chores for the public. We believe in Progress, but when we get on the train we go only as far as our ticket allows us, for we don't believe in beating our way to Utopia. We get our opinions as we get our household supplies, according to our daily needs, and on the cash-and-carry plan. We are the kind of people whose existence in large numbers is taken for granted in every scheme of democratic control. Without us trial by jury or universal suffrage would be impossible. We make free institutions work — so far as they do work.

'Our job is not spectacular, but we keep

everlastingly at it. We are aware that our modest endeavors do not make an exciting theme for oratory. You have read the inscription on the pedestal of the statue of Wendell Phillips in the Boston Public Garden, "Whether in chains or in laurels, Liberty hath only victories." This may be true, but most of the time when we have seen Liberty she was neither in chains nor in laurels, but in working dress. She was not having her victories, but in great need of reliable assistants. We are the kind of people who are not above helping her with her chores. Some of us have been working like slaves for free institutions, and mighty little recognition do we get for our labor.

'The trouble with our class is that nobody takes us seriously. There are so many of us that we can't get a fair hearing. When people discuss what they call the Social Unrest, they always talk about the grievances of minorities. The intellectuals don't have all the appreciation they deserve; the unemployed don't have all the work they demand. If a man is a bigot or a crank or an obstructionist, if he is a superman or a pseudo-superman or an underdog, he will be heard. Minorities have a way of organizing effectively, and they adopt more or less terroristic methods. People pay attention to them because they have a way of making themselves dangerous. In the most frigidly polite circles nobody would ignore the presence of a rattle-snake with nine rattles.

'It's because we are so patient and make so few unreasonable demands that we are treated so shamefully. We are looked upon as negligible quantities by the very people who wouldn't know what to do if we were to go on a general strike. They think we will go on doing our various duties no matter how we are treated. Every one who wants to get a reputation for cleverness picks upon us. The intelligentsia taunt us for our mediocrity. When we try to cheer up and make the best of a hard situation our critics call us smug. When we are interested in our local community we are called provincial. The eager radicals scorn us because we don't go far enough. The high-and-dry conservatives chide us for going at all. The cocksure reformers scold us whatever we do. Even the publicity agents chide us because they try to sell more new ideas than our market can absorb, they encounter what they call "sales resistance."

'Here is an advertisement which appeared in a popular magazine: "Ninety per cent of the population is behind the times. Eight per cent is ahead of them. Two per cent leads the way. Are you of the two per cent?"

'Of course we know the way one can qualify as a two-per-center: by paying two dollars and a half for the magazine. But I won't accept the offer. I don't admit that ninety per cent of the population is behind the times. We are the times.

'So far as the things that are most vital to democracy are concerned, we are all right. We have good horse sense and love of fair play, and enough intelligence to make an interesting society. Ninety-nine out of a hundred people believe in making this the land of the free and the home of the brave. Why don't we make a better job of it?'

'That has often puzzled me,' I said.

'Of course it has,' said the Grand Vermicularius. 'You are an average man. You mean well. But with reasonable and tolerant citizens like yourself in the vast majority, what do we see? The most amazing outbreaks of intolerance and bigotry take place and you do nothing to prevent them. You seem to be helpless and do nothing but grumble over the

excesses of narrow-minded minorities. In
every group, social, political, or religious,
there are the bigots and the non-bigots. The
non-bigots have the numerical preponder-
ance, but they seem to be lacking in back-
bone. They allow themselves to be misrepresented. It's because they are unorgan-
ized. People of good sense and good temper,
I believe, ought to be organized in one big
union. Then they would have some influence.

'I thought of many forms of organization,
but they were all too amiable to be effective.
One day I had a talk with a friend of mine
who was an ex-Dragon. "The trouble with
your friends," he said, "is that nobody is
afraid of you. You put your trust in great
moral principles. But a great moral principle
never scared any one. It doesn't jump out at
a fellow as he is going through the woods, and
clutch him with its skinny fingers and make
him promise to be good. Nobody thinks
about it as an old witch who will catch him if
he doesn't watch out. And the consequence
is that he doesn't watch out. He makes a
polite bow to the great moral principle, and
then thinks no more about it. I believe you
fellows," said the ex-Dragon, "could put us

all out of business if you understood more about human nature."

'That set me thinking. I saw that plain common sense mustn't be made too plain, and I made up my mind to found a new organization. Our organization, to be effective, must have something cryptic about it. As the ex-Dragon said, we must keep people guessing. There must be a salutary mixture of publicity and secrecy. Hence the I.O.T.W.

'The first thing was to get a totem and a slogan. All the larger quadrupeds like the Moose and Elk and Lion had been already preëmpted. Then I remembered Shakespeare's remark that "the smallest worm will turn, being trodden on." In a flash the whole thing came to me. I would organize the Independent Order of Turning Worms. Our insignia would be a worm rampant, with the motto "I turn." Again I turned to Shakespeare and found, "A certain convocation of politic worms." Just the name for the Supreme Council which would meet in the Thrice-Hidden Burrow of the Great Awareness.

'This Great Awareness is the fundamental principle of our order. The modest man who asks only to be allowed to think his own thoughts and go about his business is often imposed upon by his aggressive associates. But when his rights as an individual are trampled upon the humblest member of the I.O.T.W. is not only aware of it, but is able instantly to make others aware of his awareness. He has only to give the secret sign of our order to be sure of sympathy and assistance in his chosen work of minding his own business, for, as I have said, we are everywhere.

'The phenomenal growth of our order is explained by the transparent simplicity of our aims and the well-calculated mystery of our proceedings. You will notice a change that takes place wherever we establish our Burrows. I was talking with an efficient salesman the other day. He was complaining that he had lately encountered a great deal of sales resistance. I smiled because I knew the reason. He had taken a course in psychology and had learned the art, by the right appeal to the subconscious ego of his prospect, of making him buy any amount of goods that he didn't want. But psychology is a game two can play at. We have established classes in our Burrows of preventive psychology.

'Our order cuts across all the lines to which people are accustomed. But there is one thing which unites us in a far-flung brotherhood. Each one is prepared to assert his individuality against the tyranny of the little group of which he is a loyal unit. Our members do not renounce any of their old affiliations — they only make new ones. We are all we used to be and something more. We are Jesuits, Jews, Baptists, Republicans, Middle-Westerners, Socialists, Down-East Yankees, realtors, motorists, behaviorists, vegetarians, professors, capitalists, single-taxers, Congressmen, ministers, archæologists, and simplified spellers. We allow ourselves to be classified and card-catalogued and psychoanalyzed in all sorts of ways, for the benefit of statistical science. We answer the questionnaires that are sent to us.

'All members of the order are pledged to keep an open mind. The Commandment which we promise to obey is one that has been much neglected by overzealous persons who are anxious to reform everybody but themselves. It is the Ninth Commandment — "Thou shalt not bear false witness against they neighbor." Our Chaplain, who is officially known as the Worshipful Glowworm,

preached a sermon on the Great Commandment which is placed in the hands of all
initiates. In this sermon he upheld the thesis
that the best way to avoid bearing false witness against your neighbor is to be willing to
listen to your neighbor when he is bearing
witness to his own opinions and manner of
life. You should be willing to hear him out.
You bear false witness against him when you
draw inferences from his statements and attribute them to him. He is not responsible
for your logic. You should also learn, said
the Chaplain, that it's bad manners to call
names, but if you must do so you must know
what the names mean. This is a rule of the
order. It is enforced by an officer known as
the Formidable Nomenclator. He conducts
the much-dreaded Ordeal of the Dictionary.
Above his tribunal is a Shakespearean motto
— "Define, define, well-educated infant."
Words like "syndicalist, socialist, materialist
anarchist, bolshevist, puritan, Christian,
pagan," and the like must be defined before
they are used. Adjectives derived from collective nouns like "Jesuitical, Methodistical,
Jewish," and the like are closely inspected to
see that no pestiferous associations are attached to them.

'We do not allow members to indulge in wholesale accusations such as are to be found in Alexander Pope's couplet:

> Is he a churchman, then he's fond of power.
> A Quaker sly, a Presbyterian sour.

In each case the indictment must be so drawn up as to point to a single individual and not to include all the members of the group to which he belongs. One sour Presbyterian must not be allowed to destroy the reputation of a whole Presbytery which, but for him, may be all sweetness and light. You have no idea how many letters I receive from persons in all parts of the country who have been braced up by our order. Here is one from a high-school teacher:

'Blessings on you, honored Vermicularius, for what you have done for me. I am one of that hopeless race of men whose misfortune it is to teach American history with some understanding of the subject. Moreover, I was rash enough to try to make my pupils understand it too. In making the attempt I got in wrong with some of the most influential persons in the community. One of my pupils reported that I had said that George Washington was a revolutionist. His angry parent came to me and said that I was no fit person to teach children — I was putting ideas into their heads. I very tactlessly told him that

that was what I was here for. I afterward explained that I was referring to the American Revolution and not to the Russian, but the harm had been done. He replied that it was not what I said but the way I said it that made the mischief. His children came home and reported the way Samuel Adams and Patrick Henry talked, just as if they were real people. It sounded seditious. There must be some kind of propaganda behind it.

'Now, if there is anything that makes the cold shivers run down the spines of some of our citizens it's that word. Tennyson tells how the Northern Farmer riding to the mill heard his horse's hoofs beating out a single word: —

Property, property, property — that's what I 'ears
  him say.

These nervous citizens hear another refrain which has to them a sinister sound:

Propaganda, propaganda, propaganda — that's what
  I hear them say.

Now I wasn't interested in any propaganda. I wanted to teach American history and make it a live subject.

'Just as I had made up my mind to give up teaching and go to raising chickens, I told my troubles to a member of the school board whom I had most feared because he was spoken of as belonging to the old guard. I told him that I had no ulterior motives. I wasn't trying to influence the next election. My pupils won't be of voting age anyway for four or five years, and by that time there will be a new set of issues. All I wanted to do was to teach American history.

'That's what we hired you for, wasn't it?' he said. Then he gave me the mystic sign of awareness and told me about the new order.

'"More than half the school board belong to it and a lot of the parents," he went on. "When your persecutors bring your case before the board they'll get a big jolt. We have agreed among ourselves to give up the attempt to make education safe for ignorance. We have turned."

'Of late,' said the Grand Vermicularius, 'there are evidences that the professors in our colleges are giving up their attitude of lofty detachment and are joining us. They have found that that academic freedom of which they were so proud cannot be maintained as a matter of course and by their own unaided efforts. They need assistance from the community.

'It's hard for the learned to meet the new conditions. Up to within a few centuries academic freedom meant that scholars could say anything they pleased so long as they said it in Latin. The difficulties of an unknown tongue protected them from the attacks of their enemies, as the Alps protect the Swiss. With the grammatical passes strongly

held, the learned in their linguistic fastness
preserved their freedom during ages of bar-
barism. But now that they must speak in the
vulgar tongue their protection is gone.

'Academic freedom is seen to be a part of
the general struggle against meddlesome
tyranny. As Longfellow puts it, against "all
that hinders or impedes the action of the
nobler will." The professor is a man who
professes; he must make common cause with
business men, plucky politicians, conscientious plumbers, market gardeners, and all
other persons who insist on actually doing
what they profess to do. If a gas-fitter professes to make a tight joint, he resents the
interference of a boss who orders him to do
poor work. If a member of our order professes to teach biology, he teaches Simon-
pure biology. He refuses to have anything
to do with biology with a string tied to it.
And it's so with all the other arts and sciences.
The professors these days are with us to a
man. Our Burrows are full of them.

'If you have always lived in an atmosphere
of intellectual freedom you have no idea of
the loneliness of hapless men who have the
misfortune to be born with a good understanding without any opportunities for culti-

vating it, and who live in a community hostile
to the interchange of ideas. They are often
ostracized for opinions which they do not
hold.

'Here is a letter from a man in Arkome-
soropilis, Arkansas:

'I have long been known as the Village Atheist.
You know what that means. It came about
through my reading a sizable book, a rare inci-
dent in our neighborhood. The author said he
was a deist, and I said that I agreed with his
views. So I was at once dubbed an atheist. I
didn't mean to go that far, but it wasn't any use
for one man to go against the crowd in the matter of a name. It won't do in our town to make
too nice distinctions. It is not our way. I got to
feel pretty much alone. But since a Burrow of
the I.O.T.W. has been formed here, I've had, for
the first time, what might be called intellectual
fellowship. It's been a real treat to talk things
over with people who don't expect you to agree
with them. I find that I do agree with them more
than I thought and I'm not so queer as I prided
myself on being.

'The other night the Deputy Nomenclator —
who, by the way, is a Deacon in the Fundamen-
talist Church at the Four Corners — sprang the
Dictionary Test upon us. We all recited in concert
the ritual, "Define, define, well-educated infant."
This put us in the right mood. He discovered
that the word "deist" meant a person who be-

lieves that there is a god, and atheist is one who
believes that there isn't. "If that's the case,"
said the Deacon, "it makes quite a difference. If
you are a deist I don't see why we should keep on
calling you an atheist."

'After that we got to be quite chummy. We
found we had a lot of ideas in common and he
took quite a shine to me. After a time I found
that he was making a deep study of the dictionary. One day he came to me and said, "I've found
fifty-seven varieties of Christians, and I haven't
got more than half through the book. You are
probably one of the kinds I haven't found out
about yet. If you don't mind, I'm going to take
a chance and call you a Christian — at least
you'll let me put you on the waiting list." I said
I didn't mind and I'd like to catalogue him as a
liberal, of a hard-shell variety. He said he didn't
mind. So he keeps on going to his kind of church
and I keep on not going — but we get along first
rate.

'Some of the more zealous members of the
Klan thought we were going too far in taking
everybody in and breaking down the usual antipathies, and thought they would run us out of
town. So one night they put on their hoods and
broke into our Burrow. They thought they were
going to intimidate us, but when they looked
around and saw a lot of their big men seated with
us and wearing the insignia of the worm rampant,
they changed their tune. You see, we in Arko-
mesoropilis are great joiners, and there was
nothing to hinder any one from enjoying the

hospitality of both the Klan and the Burrow. Some thought the double membership did them good. They thought it kind of steadied them. So we asked the young fellows who had come to run us out of town to take off their hoods and stay for refreshments. They did so, and, as the saying is, a very enjoyable time was had.

'I could read to you a great many more letters,' said the Grand Vermicularius, 'but I think you have got a general idea of what we are up to.'

'Your idea,' I said, 'seems to be a very reasonable one, but couldn't you get it over to the public without so much mystification?'

'The ex-Dragon thinks not,' said the Grand Vermicularius.

THE UNFAILING CHARM OF SOME NOVELS

I EMPHASIZE the word 'some.' I do not say that all novels have charm. I am aware that there is a severe school of novelists who would resent this idea. They insist that they do not aim to please us, but rather to show us life in all its drab reality. And if anything has to be sacrificed, it will not be the drabness.

Once people in the attempt to praise a history or biography would say, 'It is as fascinating as a novel.' And moralists would warn the young against works of fiction by saying that they made sin alluring. The novelists of the ultra-serious school are not open to this accusation. They not only do not make sin alluring — they see to it that nothing is alluring.

To those who prefer to take their fiction thus sadly, I have nothing to say. But most of us, I am sure, prefer that a novel should have charm. The question then arises, In what does the charm consist?

Why is it that we take up one novel that may be very carefully written, but it makes no particular impression upon us? Very soon we forget all about it. We take up another and it is a happy experience, so happy that from time to time we repeat it.

There are books which are never exhausted. We feel of them as did Keats of

All lovely tales that we have heard or read:
An endless fountain of immortal drink,
Pouring unto us from the heaven's brink.

What is the secret of charm? Many people take it for granted that it lies in the subject which the author chooses. There are novels which deal with pleasant subjects and others with subjects that are gloomy or repellent. A novel may be realistic or romantic or historical. It may deal with business or sex or politics, with low life or with high life. But in none of these things lies the secret of charm. The charm, if it exists at all, must be sought in only one place — the author's own mind.

The word 'fiction' tells its own story. It is literally something made. Who makes it? Obviously the author. What does he make it out of? Out of materials which he finds in his own mind. His work is a figment of his imagination. Its value depends on the kind of imagination that he happens to have.

What a novelist does is to invite me to
make a pleasure excursion through the more
interesting portions of his own mind. If the
day is fine, I accept the invitation. I am in
holiday humor and am prepared for all kinds
of haps and mishaps. He is not showing me
my world — I can see that for myself. He is
showing me his world. It is the world that is
created by his imagination. If what he has
to offer isn't worth seeing, he can't shift the
responsibility for its dullness and dreariness
on the universe. It is he who is dull and
dreary, not the subject he chooses.

Let us carry the analysis a little further.
We say that a novel is the work of *creative*
imagination. What does the novelist create
in order to charm us? It is not enough to
create a character; he must also create a
world in which that character can move
about freely. Here is where many clever
novelists fail. They analyze a single character, but they do not make us realize the
world that is behind it and around it. It is a
picture without a background. The character is like the contents of a thermos bottle
— kept cold because it is surrounded by a
vacuum. Now in real life no person is seen
apart from his environment. His feet are on

the earth; there is air for him to breathe, friends and enemies to meet; and they are as real as he is.

We say of some novels that they are without atmosphere. That suggests something in regard to the writer's mind, not only as to the quality of it, but as to the quantity of it. We are told that the reason why the moon hasn't any atmosphere to speak of is that it isn't big enough to hold what atmosphere it once had. The power of its gravitation is not enough to keep the airy particles from flying off into space. It is the same with the mind.

The atmosphere of many novels is murky and there is low visibility. The author has to explain his meaning or we lose it. The great novelist has a sense of space. He is carefree. He can afford to let his characters alone. He doesn't nag them.

Then, too, there must be space in which the characters that are created may freely move about. This necessity is overlooked by those who are interested chiefly in the analysis of character. A single person taken out of his natural environment may be studied and his reactions noted. A laboratory, if properly equipped, need not be very roomy. But it takes more space if a person is to live and bring up a family.

The mind of the novelist must have amplitude. His mind is the sky, 'than all it holds more vast, more high.' Beneath the ferment of the writer's mind the beings whom he has created live and act, each after his own kind, but we see them always as a part of something greater than themselves. Says the Hebrew sage, 'He hath set the world in their heart.' The great novelist is not so much a man of the world as a man in whom the world is. In his wide, comprehending intelligence there is for everything a season, and he hath made everything beautiful in its time.

It is one thing to see a wild animal in a cage in a menagerie. It is another thing to see it in its native habitat. We do not see men and women realistically till we see them where they belong, working out their destinies unconscious of any alien observer. Each says, like the Shunammite woman, 'I dwell among mine own people.'

The matter of sufficient mind space is likely to be neglected by the writer of problem novels. When a novelist takes a problem that is too big for him, he is likely to become peevish. When at the end of his book the problem is unsolved, he dismisses it in a petulant way: 'There, I've done my best, and you see what a mess we are in. There isn't any way out.'

But, after all, the situation may not be so bad as it seems to him. Perhaps the problem is not so much an individual problem as a social problem, and he has not given its larger aspects any attention. There must be time and space for any true solution. It is only when the big problem gets into a too contracted mind that the case seems desperate. It thrashes about like a whale stranded in a shallow bay. What the whale needs is not a friendly visitor to give it advice. It demands less sand and more sea room. And what the moral problem needs is more mind room than the author is possessed of.

It was the lack of sufficiently broad background that, in my judgment, prevented Samuel Butler's 'Way of All Flesh' from being a really great novel. The author had a thesis. He was intent on proving that the family is an institution that is not what it is cracked up to be. He is irritated by his discovery of domestic infelicities. Now it is not a new discovery that sons do not always honor their fathers and mothers, not to say their uncles and their aunts. This was known to ancient historians.

The writers who are able to enlist the interest of successive generations are those who are able to invest familiar scenes with a charm which belongs to their own natures. We have the sense that the mind of the writer is bigger than the thing he is writing about. We are made to see in a new light things which we had despised.

That a certain town is dull I can well believe. But that it can be amusingly dull, deliciously dull, with all manner of delicate variations in its dullness, is a delightful discovery. It takes the genius of Jane Austen to make us see this.

This matter of mental roominess is comparative; it consists of a due proportion in the parts. In order to have charm it is not necessary that the author's mind should be big enough to take in the whole world, but it must be big enough to take in the people and the society of which he writes, and to allow the characters considerable elbow room. There was Anthony Trollope. He could hardly be called a great novelist, but he created an atmosphere. A more worldly-minded set of people than the Trollopians it would be hard to find. They were chock-full of prejudices, they were narrow-minded, and most of them were undeniably smug. Their ideas about religion and politics were conventional to the last degree, and yet we enjoy their acquaintance. They do not get on one's nerves. There is a certain congruousness between them and their environment. There is an atmosphere of good-natured worldliness that covers a multitude of sins. Trollope was not a great novelist, but his mind, at any rate, was bigger than any of his characters. It was roomy enough to contain a whole society without crowding. These people were under no constraint; they were perfectly at home.

Thackeray, to one who belongs to his cult, produces the same impression. To be sure, he likes to interrupt his characters in order to give his own opinion. But he does this as the moderator in the town meeting, who leaves the chair to give his fellow townsmen a piece of his mind. When he takes the floor he is no longer moderator. So when Thackeray indulges in one of his asides we do not think of him as the author of 'Vanity Fair,' but as one of the characters in it.

The novelists who have power to charm us always have a good-natured ease in the presence of their subject. They have a large tolerance for human imperfectness, like the good curate:

> ... When religious sects ran mad,
> He held, in spite of all his learning,
> That if a man's belief is bad,
> It will not be improved by burning.

Just now we have a school of American novelists who seem to have a grievance. America, instead of being a stimulus to their imagination, seems to be an incubus. It is just a little more than they can bear.

What kind of country is this we live in? I confess that when I take a little journey across this continent I always return with a sense of exhilaration. For one thing, there is so much of it — and it isn't finished. When I take up books of a serious nature — sober histories, tables of statistics, bank clearances, reports of scientific and philanthropic societies, city-planning boards — I get the impression that a great many things need to be improved, but that there are vast numbers of eager and right-minded people on the job.

When I listen to the earnest exhortations

of moral reformers, I get the impression that this is a country where sin aboundeth. But it is possible that 'where sin aboundeth, grace doth much more abound.'

It is only when I turn to what used to be called 'light literature' that clouds settle down and deep depression comes upon my spirits. A group of talented writers are intent on showing up their less talented fellow citizens. To this end they give us studies of life in the American small town, on the farm, and in the crowded city. Over the gateway of each community we see the inscription, 'All hope abandon, ye who enter here.' Life is shown to be not only commonplace, but hopelessly, irremediably commonplace. We have a desolating sense of moral aridity, undue nervous tension, morbid self-consciousness, a fear of public opinion, a dearth of private opinion, a furtive interest in the forbidden, a fierce absorption in business, a futile gregariousness in the pursuit of pseudoculture. The small town is treated as if it were a disease. The city is a complication of diseases.

Is this realism? Yes, in the sense that the picture of the fauna of Africa in the old-fashioned geography book was realistic.

There, crowded upon a single page, were all
the animals of the Dark Continent — lions,
elephants, gorillas, hippopotamuses, croco-
diles, jackals — all terrible to behold; while,
as if to emphasize their terrors, there was
a pacifistic giraffe looking down upon them
with a futile smile, as much as to say, 'It's
a pity that these wild beasts are so blood-
thirsty, but that's the way they are made.'
But the small boy who got his ideas of the
continent from the picture would be unduly
alarmed. All these animals could be found
in Africa, but they were not all in one place.
Africa is a large country, and there are sec-
tions where a person could walk for a whole
day without running much risk of being
eaten up by a lion.

To picture a stupid, weak, commonplace
character may show artistic skill, but the
work fails if the impression is conveyed that
everybody is that way. A picture must have
light and shade, and they must be properly
arranged to be a work of art.

Don't you think 'Main Street' was very
realistic? Yes, and so was 'Babbitt,' and so
is 'Elmer Gantry.' But they are presented
without charm. The trouble is really in Mr.
Sinclair Lewis's mind. He is not able to look

at them humorously and understandingly. He is fidgety. One feels as one does at a dinner party when it is evident that all is not going well with the hostess and she is not able to conceal her uneasiness.

When I first took up 'Main Street' I was prepared to enjoy the people. I knew they would be just ordinary people. But I couldn't enjoy their idiosyncrasies when I saw how Mr. Sinclair Lewis felt about them. He evidently thought that such a place as Gopher Prairie ought not to exist. He was acutely conscious of its manifold shortcomings. It did not appreciate what it ought to have appreciated, and it appreciated that which it ought not to have appreciated, and there was no health in it. Just as I was trying to get on good terms with the community, I would look up and see Mr. Sinclair Lewis fidgeting and saying to himself, 'Isn't it too bad! No art, no manners, no spontaneity, no free intelligence, no cosmopolitan culture — just Main Street.'

Then I turn to Henry Fielding. It happens that none of these fine things are in the world Fielding created for our enjoyment. To most of his characters Gopher Prairie would seem a modern Athens, a lofty intellectual center,

pulsating with sensibility. Squire Western
and Tow-wouse, the innkeeper, and their
boon companions cared for none of these
things. Had a high-strung young woman,
recently graduated from a state university,
landed among these hearty, non-intellectual
folks and attempted to improve their minds,
she would have longed for the more appre-
ciative society of Main Street. It never occurred to any of Fielding's folks that they
should be improved. Their prejudices could
not be weeded out by a newly married lady
recently arrived among them. They were too
deeply rooted in the nature of things — their
things. The minister of the First Church on
Main Street might not be an intellectual
giant or a man of great refinement, but he
would seem so in comparison with Fielding's
Parson Trulliber.

His voice was loud and hoarse, and his accent
extremely broad. To complete the whole, he had
a stateliness in his gait, when he walked, not unlike that of a goose.

We are made to see Trulliber as he was in
the bosom of his family:

Mr. Trulliber being informed that somebody
wanted to speak with him, immediately slipped

off his apron, and clothed himself in an old night-gown, being the dress in which he always saw his company at home. . . . He laid violent hands on Adams, and dragged him into the hog-sty, which was indeed but two steps from his parlour-window. They were no sooner arrived there, than he cried out, 'Do but handle them: step in, friend: art welcome to handle them, whether dost buy or no.' At which words, opening the gate, he pushed Adams into a pig-sty, insisting on it that he should handle them before he would talk one word with him.

Adams had come on business unconnected with hogs, but that made no difference. Trulliber is all that a clergyman ought not to be, yet somehow, seeing his burly figure in the pigpen where he belongs, one is not de-pressed in spirits. Trulliber is Trulliber, and I am more amused than offended when he rejects Parson Adams's attempt to improve him.

'Dost preach to me?' replied Trulliber: 'dost pretend to instruct me in my duty? . . . I would not advise thee,' says Trulliber, 'to say that I am no Christian: I won't take it of you; for I believe I am as good a man as thyself.'

I do not fret over Trulliber when I see him as a part of Fielding's ample world. He is a blot on the landscape, but fortunately it is a large and smiling landscape and can stand a good many such blots.

We are out of doors in a pleasant English countryside. We meet all sorts of people. Most of them have little refinement, but they have a heartiness that is refreshing. We trudge along in all weathers. We stop at inns where there are usually some adventures. We meet strangers who suddenly become confidential.

Squire Western would be intolerable anywhere else, but we enjoy seeing him as he goes storming over his broad acres. He belongs there, and he knows it, and so do his dependents. And we like to hear him talk. It isn't every day that we can get so close to a coarse country squire of the eighteenth century.

As to his daughter Sophia, she has her sore trials, but she is a buxom creature blessed with good health. When, under great provocation and in accordance with the fashion of the day, she faints, she is well looked after. 'Mrs. Western and a great number of servants soon came to the assistance of Sophia, with water, cordials, and everything necessary on those occasions.' In a few minutes she was as well as ever. This is as it should be.

In Fielding's world they had hard knocks, but great power of recuperation. There was always plenty of fresh air, and a refreshing sense of fair play. This goes a long way in keeping every one in good condition. When we are tired of problems, there is pleasure in looking over Fielding's chapter headings:

An apology for all heroes who have good stomachs.

A friendly conversation in a kitchen.

A dialogue between the landlady and Susan the chambermaid.

The adventure of a beggar-man.

This is not high life, but we are in good company so long as we are with Henry Fielding.

To reveal this ever-changing world is the task of genius.

What Fielding did for the English countryside of the eighteenth century and Chaucer did for the England of the fourteenth century, Cervantes did for Spain in the sixteenth century, Walter Scott did for his own Scotland, Dickens did for the England of the nineteenth century, Victor Hugo did for Revolutionary France, Tolstoy did for the prerevolutionary Russia, Joseph Conrad did for the seas.

They did more than analyze or describe individuals — they created, or rather re-created, the times in which these people lived.

Dickens is an example of the way in which the limitations of a writer's own mind affect his power to portray character. Dickens was a humorist, but first of all he was an Englishman. He loved his country and understood its people. He loved to prowl around in the dark places of London and make the acquaintance of queer and shabby people. He understood them well enough to know that they had pleasures as well as sorrows of their own. Their idiosyncrasies do not irritate us. We see them through the atmosphere of humorous tolerance. There were all kinds of Englishmen, but England was a very interesting place to live in.

But when Dickens crossed the Atlantic and attempted to find literary material in America, a change came over his spirit. He was no longer at ease. He felt as the old prophet felt when he was considering the sins of people he didn't like — 'By day and by night: and it shall be a vexation only to understand the report. For the bed is shorter than that a man can stretch himself on it:

and the covering narrower than that he can wrap himself in it.'

Martin Chuzzlewit lands in New York and travels to Eden on the Mississippi. In spite of all the efforts of Mark Tapley to be jolly under all circumstances, there is not a single pleasant adventure. The circumstances are too much for them. It is a land where every prospect displeases and man becomes more vile as they go west. What a vulgar lot of people they meet — the reporters of 'The Rowdy Journal,' the Honorable Jefferson Brick, Mr. Lafayette Kettle, Mrs. Hominy, and the rest.

Yet, when we come to think about it, they were no more vulgar than the people Dickens was familiar with at home. The manners of the Podsnaps, the Todgers, the Micawbers, were not above reproach. The difference was that he found the vulgar Englishman amusing, but the vulgar American was odious.

When Mr. Boffin acquires a sudden competence, we sympathize with him in his desire to attain culture with equal celerity by employing a literary gentleman with a wooden leg to read to him.

But Martin Chuzzlewit has no tolerance for the efforts of Mrs. Jefferson Brick to improve her mind gregariously by going to lectures on the Philosophy of the Soul on Wednesday, the Philosophy of Crime on Monday, the Philosophy of Government on Tuesday, and the Philosophy of Vegetables on Friday.

On hearing this laudable programme, Martin was plunged into melancholy. 'As soon as Martin was left alone ... he felt so thoroughly dejected and worn out, that he even lacked the energy to crawl upstairs to bed.' Yet Mrs. Jefferson Brick had her good points; only Dickens could not see them. He was too homesick.

How pleasant in England to obscure the incongruities between the names of things and the realities! Not so on the Mississippi. When New Thermopylæ turns out to be lacking in classic grace, we find that it is not only a calamity but an insult. Mrs. Hominy had no right to speak of it in such glowing terms.

It was almost night when they came alongside the landing-place — a steep bank with an hotel, like a barn, on the top of it; a wooden store or two; and a few scattered sheds.

'You sleep here to-night, and go on in the morning, I suppose, ma'am,' said Martin.

'Where should I go on to?' cried the mother of the modern Gracchi.

'To New Thermopylæ.'

'My! Ain't I there?' said Mrs. Hominy.

Martin looked for it all round the darkening panorama; but he couldn't see it, and was obliged to say so.

'Why, that's it!' cried Mrs. Hominy, pointing to the sheds just mentioned.

'That!' exclaimed Martin.

Let us take an English scene and compare the impression with that of an American scene.

Supper was not yet over, when there arrived at the Jolly Sandboys two more travellers, bound for the same haven as the rest, who had been walking in the rain for some hours, and came in shining and heavy with water. One of these was the proprietor of a giant and a little lady without legs or arms, who had jogged forward in a van, the other, a silent gentleman who earned his living by showing tricks upon the cards, and who had rather deranged the natural expression of his countenance by putting small leaden lozenges into his eyes and bringing them out at his mouth, which was one of his professional accomplishments. The name of the first of the new-comers was Vuffin; the other, probably as a pleasant satire upon his ugliness, was called Sweet William. To render them as comfortable as he could, the landlord bestirred himself nimbly, and in a very short time both gentlemen were perfectly at their ease.

And so are we — and it is Dickens who puts us at our ease. We at once make ourselves at home and it occurs to us that it is a rare opportunity to sit here in the bar and listen to Mr. Vuffin and his friend talk shop.

Mr. Vuffin, it appears, has a giant who has outlived his usefulness. He thinks it better business to carry him about in his van, without exhibiting, than to turn him off.

'It's better that than letting 'em go upon the parish or about the streets,' said Mr. Vuffin. 'Once make a giant common, and giants will never draw again. Look at wooden legs. If there was only one man with a wooden leg, what a property *he'd* be!'

'So he would!' observed the landlord and Short both together. 'That's very true.'

'Instead of which,' pursued Mr. Vuffin, 'if you was to advertise Shakespeare played entirely by wooden legs, it's my belief you wouldn't draw a sixpence.'

'I don't suppose you would,' said Short. And the landlord said so too. . . .

While Mr. Vuffin and his two friends smoked their pipes and beguiled the time with such conversation as this, the silent gentleman sat in a warm corner, swallowing, or seeming to swallow, six-pennyworth of half-pence for practice . . . without paying any regard whatever to the company.

They were certainly not a highly intellectual company — but somehow we get the general impression of good cheer. Even the silent gentleman who was practicing his art was enjoying himself according to his lights.

Compare this with the scene on the steamboat which was carrying Martin Chuzzlewit to Eden on the Mississippi.

On, through the weary day and melancholy night, beneath the burning sun, and in the mist and vapor of the evening; on, until return appeared impossible, and restoration to their home a miserable dream. They had now but few people on board; and these few were as flat, as dull and stagnant, as the vegetation that oppressed their eyes. No sound of cheerfulness or hope was heard; no pleasant talk beguiled the tardy time; no little group made common cause against the dull depression of the scene. But that, at certain periods, they swallowed food together from a common trough, it might have been old Charon's boat, conveying melancholy shades to judgment.

We can think of Dickens escaping from the melancholy company in the cabin of the Mississippi steamboat and standing on the deck as the boat scraped across the mud bars and the man casting the lead called out, 'Mark three! Mark twain!' It was a doleful sound.

But there was a boy about that time sprawling on the banks of that great river who found it a mighty interesting place. To be a pilot on a Mississippi River steamboat seemed the pinnacle of human greatness. When he made his first voyage, he was intoxicated by the talk.

All pilots are tireless talkers, when gathered together, and as they talk only about the river they are always understood and are always interesting. Your true pilot cares nothing about anything on earth but the river, and his pride in his occupation surpasses the pride of kings.

They went on talk-talk-talking. Meantime, the thing that was running in my mind was, 'Now, if my ears hear aright, I have not only to get the names of all the towns and islands and bends, and so on, by heart, but I must get up a warm personal acquaintanceship with every old snag and one-limbed cottonwood and obscure woodpile that ornaments the banks of this river for twelve hundred miles; and more than that, I must actually know where these things are in the dark.' . . .

'My boy,' said Mr. Bixby, 'there's only one way to be a pilot, and that is to get this entire river by heart.'

It was a whole world of romance that opened up to the Missouri boy as he heard the leadsman repeating, 'M-a-r-k three! M-a-r-k three! Quarter-less-three! Half twain Quarter twain! M-a-r-k twain!'

That Dickens found the Mississippi River steamboat and its passengers inexpressibly dreary and dull, and that Mark Twain found in the same place and among the same people rollicking humor and dry wit and the spirit of adventure, does not prove that Mark Twain had more humor. It only proves that he was more at home.

Mr. Bixby's maxim that to be a pilot on the Mississippi one must get the whole river by heart and get up a warm personal acquaintance with every old snag and wood-pile applies to the novelist. It is not enough that he can describe one particular sand bar on which his characters are stranded. He must know the river, and understand the great currents, and sympathize with the people who are floating upon the stream. He must see each part in relation to the whole.

Homer tells us that in the camp on the Trojan plain there was an ill-favored, sharp-tongued Greek named Thersites. He was an unpopular character and deservedly so. He spent his time in speaking scornfully of the heroes and belittling their exploits. If Thersites had been a literary man his remarks would have made good copy. The Iliad of Thersites would have been considered spicy.

Shakespeare amused himself by imagining
how the Homeric heroes would have been
described by the vitriolic critics. Thersites
is made to express himself in the sixteenth-
century language of vituperation.

Agamemnon — 'an honest fellow enough,
and one that loves quails; but he has not so
much brains as ear-wax.'

Diomedes — 'a false-hearted rogue, a most
unjust knave. I will no more trust him when
he leers than I will a serpent when he hisses.'

Patroclus — 'male   varlet. . . . How   the
poor world is pestered with such waterflies,
diminutives of nature!'

Ajax — 'thou sodden-witted lord! Thou
has no more brain than I have in mine el-
bows. . . . Thou scurvy valiant ass!'

Achilles and Ajax — 'Hector shall have a
great catch, if he knock out either of your
brains. He were as good crack a fisty nut
with no kernel.'

So runs the Iliad of Thersites. But successive generations have preferred the 'Iliad'
of Homer. The old poet created a world and
filled it with gods and godlike men. Here his
heroes moved about freely. We are made to
see the windy plain of Troy. We see the little
ships that had sailed over perilous seas. We

hear the Olympian laughter from distant mountain tops. When we hear Achilles saying, 'How many misty mountains and what resounding seas separate me from my dear native land,' the distance must be measured by Homer's standard and not ours. We must not remark smugly that an airplane could cover the distance in three quarters of an hour. On the other hand, we must remember that far-darting Apollo had facilities of travel more rapid than our own. To enjoy Homer's heroes we must see them in Homer's world.

And if there is to be a great American novel, it must arise in the mind of a great American. His mind must be large enough to take in the real America. It must have wide spaces in which all sorts and conditions of men may have room to live and grow. It must have a wide hospitality for that which is still hopefully unfinished. It must have curiosity, humor, and audacity. It must have appreciation for that which is still in the rough. It must have heroes of its own and its peculiar kind of hero worship. One thing we may be sure of — it will be the work of an American Homer and not of an American Thersites.

THE END